# The Art of
# PROSE
# FICTION

### EDITED BY **RALPH H. SINGLETON**

OBERLIN COLLEGE

97024

## THE WORLD PUBLISHING COMPANY

*Cleveland and New York*

# Acknowledgments

"How Beautiful with Shoes," by Wilbur Daniel Steele. Copyright 1932 and 1959 by Wilbur Daniel Steele. Reprinted by permission of The Harold Matson Co., Inc.

"I'm a Fool," by Sherwood Anderson. Copyright © 1924 by Eleanor Anderson. Reprinted by permission of Harold Ober Associates, Incorporated.

"Paul's Case," reprinted from *Youth and the Bright Medusa* by Willa Cather, courtesy of Alfred A. Knopf, Inc.

"The Rocking-Horse Winner," by D. H. Lawrence, from *The Complete Short Stories of D. H. Lawrence*, Volume III, Compass Edition. Copyright 1933 by the Estate of D. H. Lawrence; © 1962 by Angelo Ravagli and Montague C. Weekly, Executors of the Estate of Frieda Lawrence Ravagli. Reprinted by permission of The Viking Press, Inc.

"The Killers," by Ernest Hemingway. "The Killers" (Copyright 1927 Ernest Hemingway; renewal copyright 1945) is reprinted with the permission of Charles Scribner's Sons from *Men Without Women*, by Ernest Hemingway.

"The Circus," by Katherine Anne Porter. Copyright 1935, 1963 by Katherine Anne Porter. Reprinted from her volume *The Leaning Tower and Other Stories*, by permission of Harcourt, Brace & World, Inc.

# Preface

THE READING of literature, as every teacher knows, requires considerable experience and application, with each literary genre presenting its own problems, its own difficulties. The aim of this little book is to help the student acquire the ability to read prose fiction. To this end I have presented in detail the techniques of the short story, followed by six carefully selected stories by masters of the craft.

One story, *How Beautiful with Shoes*, by Wilbur Daniel Steele, has been analyzed in detail. This explanation can serve both as a means of approaching and understanding other stories and as a model for the student's own analyses. It has been my experience over the years, shared, I am sure, by other teachers of literature, that most students find such a guide extremely helpful, if not downright necessary. At the outset of a study of literature students seldom know what to look for in reading a story, and are often completely bewildered when asked to write a story analysis.

A study of prose fiction can begin logically with the short story, rather than the novel, for a variety of reasons. A short story can be read at one sitting and discussed as a whole, whereas a novel must be read over a period of time and discussed piecemeal. In addition, all the techniques of prose fiction can be illustrated in the short story: the characters, what they are like and how the author has brought them to life; the point of view, the consciousness through which the action is presented, how it affects the selection and presentation of details; the setting, the environment, both physical and psychological, through which the characters move and which motivates their actions; the plot, the conflict of the central character, the protagonist, with others, with his environment, with himself; the theme, that unifying idea which becomes the controlling influence in every story—all these can be illustrated in the short story, along with such contributing factors as style and symbolism.

Moreover, the short story is, I believe, an easy and natural introduction to literature. For it deals with sense experience, people in action that is both sequential and consequential. The reader can follow the experience

v

of the characters in a story more readily than he can follow an abstract argument or the highly condensed and often highly symbolic lyrical poem. Mastery of the short story is a natural introduction to narrative poetry, for many of its techniques are similar. It is also a natural introduction to the drama, which is narrative stripped to dialogue; here the reader must supply for himself a good deal of what the stage supplies for the observer.

And finally, the short story is more familiar to most students than are other literary genres. A child frightened by a clown at a circus, a boy telling a lie and finding that he has isolated himself from the girl who has begun to be very important to him, a boy attracted by the glamor of the theatrical so that his own home seems shabby and unbearable—all these are experiences that the student can reach out and touch, even though he may never have experienced them himself.

There has been a need for a little book of short stories, coupled with a complete apparatus for reading and understanding them, with the emphasis upon close and intelligent reading. The stories in this book can easily be supplemented, if desired, and to this end I have added, in an appendix, a supplementary reading list made up of representative stories from Edgar Allan Poe to the present day, stories that can be found in *An Introduction to Literature* (The World Publishing Co., 1966).

I have also included, from that volume, biographies of the authors represented, and, more important, a glossary of literary terms, which should prove helpful to the student in the reading of critical materials.

These stories in themselves should furnish an adequate introduction to the understanding of prose fiction. Sherwood Anderson might almost be called the father of the modern short story, for his break with a stereotyped form paved the way for the diversity and experimentation that is still going on today. Willa Cather, herself an experimenter and careful artist, has produced some of the minor classics of American literature. D. H. Lawrence's story comes close to being a perfect little masterpiece of the story-telling art. Wilbur Daniel Steele won a special prize from the O. Henry Memorial Award Committee in 1921 for maintaining the highest level of merit for three years among American writers of the short story. Ernest Hemingway, winner of the Pulitzer and Nobel Prizes for literature, is undoubtedly a major figure on the scene of prose fiction, and "The Killers" is his most famous story. Katherine Anne Porter won the National Book Award for prose fiction in 1966 for her *Collected Stories*. Surely anyone who has read and studied stories by these six authors might well be said to have been introduced to the art of the short story.

It is my hope and belief that the student will thoroughly enjoy reading these stories and that the instructor will find them rewarding for study and analysis.

RALPH H. SINGLETON

# Contents

# The Art Of Prose Fiction

# Introduction

STORYTELLING is as old as the recorded history of man, but the novel and the short story as we know them now are of relatively recent origin. The novel in English was born with the rise of the middle class in the first quarter of the eighteenth century. The short story did not make its appearance until a hundred years later, in the tales of two American writers, Nathaniel Hawthorne and Edgar Allan Poe.

Poe is commonly regarded as the father of the short story because, in addition to the skillfully constructed prose tales that he published in various magazines and annuals between 1830 and 1835, he was the first to set down a clear concept of what a short story should be: a brief tale with every word aimed to bring about a single effect, a "pre-established design."

Although the short story has had outstanding practitioners in many countries, it has had its greatest popularity and development in America. That development has taken numerous directions: the well-plotted story with a realistic portrayal of men and motives; the story with a surprise or trick ending; the "local color" story; the hard-boiled story with a strictly objective approach to its presentation of characters in action; the story with a strong emphasis upon character and a consequent playing down of plot; the "slice of life" with the virtual disappearance of any organized plot structure; the story with social implications. The short story today is in a state of flux, continual experimentation, but in the hands of skillful practitioners it is a powerful instrument for saying something significant about the world in which we live.

In spite of its diversity, we can describe the short story in the following terms. As Poe has indicated, because it is short enough to be read at one sitting, it is capable of a unity of effect that the novel is unable to achieve. A single line of action that develops a single idea, or theme, is its main characteristic. This, we say, is what the story is *about*. Also, where the novel is likely to have a multiplicity of characters, the short story has few, and always one who stands out as the central figure upon whom our attention is focused. This individual, called the *protagonist*, is engaged in a conflict of some sort, the outcome of which is crucial to him, and consequently to us; for if the story is successful, we identify with him in some measure as we follow his fortunes. The experience he undergoes is so significant that it usually leaves its mark upon him; normally, we see him at the end of the story a changed individual. The pattern is infinitely various, every story presenting its own problem, worked out by the author in his own way.

To read a story with full understanding makes certain demands upon the reader. A story is made up of characters in action, and so the reader must recognize the characters' moral nature that motivates their actions. These actions grow out of an initial situation, take place in a particular setting—a physical, a social, a psychological environment—and are presented from an angle of vision that both limits and illuminates the action. A dominant idea, or theme, unfolds as the action develops—a theme often underlined by certain symbols and enforced by the author's style.

What we are leading up to is that to read a short story intelligently requires a knowledge of the techniques of prose fiction. As we consider them in detail, let us focus upon a few of the stories in the anthology, and primarily upon one story, Wilbur Daniel Steele's "How Beautiful with Shoes."

## Character

Let us first consider characters in a story. Our interest in people, the forces that move them and motivate their actions, is a primary reason for reading fiction. We are as likely to remember the characters in a story as what happened to them, for the skillful author brings to life unforgettable men and women, as real as the flesh-and-blood people we meet every day.

There is, however, one fundamental difference. A fictional character is never as complex as the people we see around us. Only a few significant traits appear in a character as he is re-created for us in the fictitious world of the short story. To use E. M. Forster's classification, the characters in a short story are "flat," not "round"; that is, they act consistently from a few well-defined traits. Why is this? No author can develop in a few thousand words many varying facets of an individual's personality. Nor is this necessary. A short story uses only those aspects of character required by the situation.

To illustrate from Steele's story, Mare Doggett, as Steele portrays her, is quite uncomplicated. She is a slow-minded, inarticulate farm girl with a natural skill in handling animals. She possesses a certain fortitude, a quiet courage when the occasion demands it. There is also the bare suggestion that she has inherited from her dead father the potential for an appreciation of beauty, symbolized by the name he gave her—Amarantha. This summarizes Mare, who is by far the most fully realized character in the story.

Ruby Herter, her fiancé, is little more than a healthy young male animal. Mrs. Doggett, Mare's mother, is merely a querulous, deaf woman. Humble Jewett, the "loony," is more complex. A demented, tortured soul, his love for beauty is at odds with his homicidal tendencies.

The simplification of the characters in a story makes them immediately intelligible and keeps their actions consistent. We expect—demand, really—the consistency that we seldom get from the people in the world around us. Calling a character in fiction "flat" is no term of reproach, no indication that he is unreal. Mare is certainly real to the reader; in fact, she is more real than if she had been presented with such a high degree of complexity that her actions would be bewildering.

Most of the characters in prose fiction are flat, even in the novel. This, as Forster goes on to state, is a great advantage to both writer and reader. "It is," says Forster, "a convenience for an author when he can strike with his full force at once, and flat characters are very useful to him, since they never need reintroducing, never run away, have not to be watched for development, and provide their own atmosphere. . . ." They are "easily remembered by the reader afterwards. They remain in his mind as unalterable, for the reason that they were not changed by circumstances; they move through circumstances, which gives them in retrospect a comforting quality, and preserves them when the book that produced them may decay."

### RECOGNIZING AND EVALUATING CHARACTER

An author presents the reader with many clues for the recognition and evaluation of character in his story. These clues are comparable to the ways by which we evaluate people in the world around us. They are:

*Action.* We judge people by the way they act, particularly in a crucial situation. What a person *does* presents convincing evidence of what he *is*. Mare's action in quietly leading the homicidal "loony" away from the house to protect her mother indicates the firm control she has over herself, which manifests itself again, later, when she is abducted by him. And the passivity with which she receives Ruby's caresses, the matter-of-fact way in which she responds to his rough humor as he yanks her head back by her braids, shows a certain phlegmatic temperament. Ruby's actions are also revealing. His aggressive masculinity becomes apparent in his treatment of Mare at the outset of the story and by the way he immediately joins the pursuing posse when taunted with the possibility that he might be afraid.

*Speech.* A person's speech, like his actions, can be very revealing. In addition to showing such things as age, nationality, education—all of which serve as identification—speech can reveal habits of mind and the reaction to people and events—both sharply indicative of character. Most of us have had the experience of overhearing a conversation between people who are total strangers to us and gaining therefrom an immediate impression of their personalities. Ernest Hemingway, in the opening scene of "The Killers," lets us listen to a conversation between two strangers and the counterman in Henry's lunchroom. The contempt, the downright nastiness, the utter disregard for personality, the blatant egotism displayed in the speech of these two strangers marks them at once as cold-blooded and vicious.

In "How Beautiful with Shoes," Mare's woodenness and natural shyness are revealed, in part, by her inarticulateness; and her comments to Humble Jewett, as he recites to her verses from the Song of Solomon, reveal her simplicity. When Humble Jewett remarks, at hearing her name, "Amarantha! That's poetry," Steele tells us that "Mare knew then that she did not know him." Of course. For his speech marked him as coming from a world different from her own. Neither Ruby nor any of his companions would have spoken like that. Ruby calls out to Mare as he sees her coming toward him across the field, "Don't run yourself out o' breath, Mare; I got all night," and his speech is as characteristic of him as the way he sits motionless on the wagon seat after she does arrive, stirring only to cut himself a fresh wad of tobacco.

*Description.* Physical appearance can, of course, be a clue to character, but the writer of fiction seldom stresses it. Details of appearance, either of feature or dress, are more often a means of identification than a means of revealing personality. Nick Adams, for example, the main character in Hemingway's "The Killers," is not described at all. The killers are, but note that they are described as though they were "twins," with their white faces and tight lips, their too-tight black overcoats buttoned across the chest, their derby hats, silk mufflers, and gloves. The intent is clearly not to show their character but to identify them as belonging to a type: paid gunmen from a large city. In "How Beautiful with Shoes" Mare is described only as "broad-fleshed," with "bare, barn-soiled feet," suggestive of a certain stodginess and that she is a farm girl. Her "yellow hair" is mentioned because, along with her name, it suggests to Humble Jewett the lines by Lovelace.

> Amarantha sweet and fair
> Braid no more that shining hair,

the name and the hair transforming flat-faced Mare Doggett into a romantic vision to the deranged former schoolteacher. Steele pictures Ruby Herter as a "big-barrelled, heavy-limbed fellow," wearing a jumper and chewing tobacco. These details, of course, do suggest character. They depict someone quite the reverse of Paul in Willa Cather's story "Paul's Case," with his thin, cramped shoulders, narrow chest, eyes marked by a hysterical brilliancy, wearing an opal tie pin and a red carnation in his buttonhole, as he stands at bay before his teachers.

*Environment.* The presentation of a person's surroundings, particularly those he deliberately chooses, including the recreations he prefers and the company he keeps, contributes to an understanding of his character. Willa Cather's description of Paul, as we have seen, gives us a clue to what he is like. But a more significant clue to his character is his reaction to his environment—his overwhelming distaste for the commonplace quality of his home, his contempt for his teachers in the high school, his reveling in the artificial glitter of the theatrical. Mare, in "How Beautiful with Shoes," is also characterized by her environment. It is what she has always known, this life on the farm, close to the soil and to elemental things. But she does not, like Paul, rebel against it. Her being a farm girl is significant in the story. It accounts for the fact that "in an animal way she knew animals," sick animals; she knew "how to move so as not to fret them." As a result, she handles Jewett, the mentally sick man, as she would handle a sick animal.

*Thoughts.* To reveal a person's thoughts is an act of omniscience. Mental states, such as nervousness, anger, horror, can be indicated by physical reactions, such as sweating palms, flushed face, rigid muscles. But thought itself cannot be so clinically observed, no matter how well we know an individual.

An author, however, can play God. This is one of the conventions of prose fiction. And presenting a person's thoughts is a very important means of characterizing him. Looking into the mind of a character, an author can reveal the secrets of his character's heart, the motivating force that drives him. We say that imputing motives to people is unfair, for how can one be sure? The writer of fiction can be sure and can open the mind of his characters to the reader at will.

In Steele's story, Mare is the only person whose thoughts are constantly revealed to us. We see everyone else almost entirely from the outside. This admission into Mare's mind plays a large part in making her, for us, a fully realized individual. When she leads the "loony" away from the house and her mother and we are allowed to learn that she is saying to herself, "He won't hurt her; it's me, not her," we become aware of the conspicuous bravery of her action. And because we can enter her mind through all the mad experience of that night with Humble Jewett and the aftermath, we can understand why she pushes Ruby out the door at the end of the story—an act that, to Ruby, is completely bewildering.

*Explanation.* Explanation is an outright statement by the author *about* his characters. It has been called "direct" characterization, in contrast to the "indirect" characterization of showing an individual in action, listening to him talk, following his thoughts, with the reader making his own inferences. Direct characterization was a common technique of the writer of prose fiction until comparatively recent times. Thackeray, for example, remarks in *Vanity Fair:* "And as we bring our characters forward, I will ask leave as a man and a brother, not only to introduce them but occasionally to step down from the platform and talk about them. . . ." Today this method of presenting character is much less common, and, in the short story, is all but outmoded. The modern short-story writer tends to screen himself out of the story by identifying himself with one of the characters. We shall discuss this method of storytelling more in detail when we consider point of view.

Willa Cather, D. H. Lawrence, Katherine Mansfield, and Wilbur Daniel Steele, among others, do talk about their characters, as well as present them dramatically. Steele, for example, tells us outright that Mare is "slow-minded" and speaks of her "native timidity." Miss Cather says that Paul "was quite accustomed to lying; found it, indeed, indispensable for overcoming friction." Actually, this direct characterization is nothing more than explanation, the author telling us directly what his characters are like.

Any or all of these methods of characterization may be used by the writer of short stories to make his people—those people who inhabit the world that he has created—live for the reader. As we read, we try to discover an individual's outstanding traits, his moral disposition, the forces that motivate him. A short story cannot show the growth and development of character. The people who appear in a short story must have their character already formed, and act in a fashion consistent with what they are. Their actions are not only consistent but inevitable. Character, we say, is fate.

## Point of View

Point of view is the angle from which a story is told, the intelligence through whose authority we view the characters and the action. Point of view is extremely important, for it accounts for the selection of a multitude of details: where we, as readers, go; what we see; whose consciousness we share. The author chooses what seems to him the most effective intelligence through which to relate the story, the one most likely to draw the reader in the most telling fashion into the emotional pull of the fictitious world that the author is creating. In doing so, he has a variety of choices.

### OMNISCIENT POINT OF VIEW

Sanctioned by long custom is the omniscient point of view. The author, as creator, tells the story from his own vantage point. He can be anywhere at any time, enter the mind of any of his characters at will, reveal their thoughts, relate the action from their physical and mental points of view, make whatever comments about them he chooses.

This omniscient point of view, although an accepted convention, runs contrary to experience, for in life everyone is limited to the testimony of his own senses and the working of his own mind. For this reason, modern writers tend to avoid the omniscient point of view in favor of a more dramatic method, one in which they do not stand between the characters and the reader. D. H. Lawrence, however, uses the omniscient point of view with complete effectiveness in "The Rocking-Horse Winner." Although Paul is the central figure, we see not only into Paul's mind but into the mind of his mother and his uncle. At the end of the story, we find ourselves not with Paul at all, but with the mother, as she opens the door of Paul's room and sees Paul rocking back and forth madly on his rocking horse and, later still, as she sits by his bedside watching him waste away, "feeling her heart had gone, turned actually into a stone."

### DRAMATIC POINT OF VIEW

At the opposite extreme from omniscience is the dramatic point of view. The writer presents the action in a purely objective fashion, as if he were at the theater watching a play. This is the point of view of the observer who relates only those details that come to him through his senses, without comment, and without entering the mind of any of his characters. Stories told from this point of view make a great demand on the reader, for he has nothing to guide his interpretation of the action. Motivation of the characters must be judged entirely by externals.

For certain types of stories and certain purposes, however, the dramatic point of view is very effective. Hemingway used the dramatic point of view in many of his early stories. Governed by a desire to avoid any explicit expression of values, Hemingway relied entirely upon the implication of the details themselves, and since dialogue is the most objective method of telling a story, leaned heavily upon dialogue. "The Killers" is a good example of the dramatic point of view. The implications of the story are not difficult to see, and yet Hemingway's objectivity is such that some readers may miss the fact that the story is Nick Adams' story.

### PERSONAL POINT OF VIEW

Between these extremes is the personal point of view. The author does not pretend to see all, know all, tell all (omniscient), nor is he an outside observer, watching the action like a member of a theater audience (dramatic); rather, he identifies himself with one actor in the drama and tells the story as it appears to him. He may tell it in the first person or the third person.

Since the personal point of view limits the writer to the actions witnessed by one individual and to this individual's thoughts and emotions, it serves as a unifying factor, a principle of selection. And because it identifies the reader with one person in the story, it helps maintain the illusion of reality that the writer is trying to create.

### FIRST PERSON

The first-person point of view is the most natural, because it is the point of view of someone recounting his own experiences. It carries an air of immediacy and authority; the reader gets the impression that he is in the center of the action, seeing things through the eyes and consciousness of the one most concerned. It reads like autobiography, not fiction. In fact, the reader must be careful not to confuse the two, not to identify the author with the character that he has created.

The account that filters through to the reader is, of course, biased. An individual telling a story in which he plays the major role cannot be objective. The nineteen-year-old hero of "I'm a Fool," for instance, tries to throw a certain amount of blame for his actions on the "dude" in the bar, whose cane and Windsor tie so irritated him that he pushed the dude around and then drank more whiskey than he had intended, just to put up a "good front." What he calls putting up a "good front," someone else might call by a quite different name. The first-person narrator, then, might be giving himself away without realizing it; he might also overrate himself or be overmodest. The reader, in other words, is expected to read between the lines, not to take the words of the protagonist at face value.

One variation of first-person point of view is the story told through the consciousness of a minor character. In a story of this kind, the narrator is merely an outsider to the main action who happens to be present at crucial times and through whose eyes and consciousness we see the action unfolding. This point of view enables an author to tell the story through someone who may not realize its significance, but who still furnishes the authenticity of an eye witness. The reader is expected to understand what is happening even though the narrator may not.

### THIRD PERSON

The most common point of view is the third-person point of view, in which we follow the action through the eye and mind of one of the characters, usually the protagonist, who is always referred to as "he" or "she." It has been called "stream of experience" (not to be confused with stream of consciousness), for the narrator *experiences* the story as it is taking place. For example, in Truman Capote's "A Tree of Night," the story is told through the consciousness of a college sophomore named Kay, who is riding the night coach of a train on her way home from her uncle's funeral. When Kay climbs aboard the train, we climb with her; as she walks through the coach looking for a seat, we walk with her; when she gets up and goes out on the observation platform, we get up and go out with her—we see everything through her consciousness. For example:

> Kay resisted a temptation to hold her nose and threaded her way carefully down the aisle, tripping once, without disaster, over a dozing fat man's protruding leg. . . .
> Embarrassed, Kay nervously opened a pack of cigarettes and lighted one. She wondered if there might not be a seat in a car up ahead. She could not bear the woman, or, for that matter, the man, another minute. But she had never before been in a remotely comparable situation.

This third-person point of view gives the illusion of reality almost as completely as does the first-person point of view, but it allows more freedom and flexibility in the telling; for the author can be outside, as well as inside, the character and can thus describe his appearance and actions as well as his thoughts and emotions. For the most part, however, it serves as an effective way for the author to screen himself out of the story by identifying with this narrator. It is also an effective way of leading the reader into the emotional center of the story, for the protagonist in a story told from this point of view is a sympathetic character, and the reader tends to identify with him—not merely to look on, but to live the experience as he lives it, to share his doubts and fears, his joys and transports. This identification is what is meant by a vicarious experience, one of the lasting pleasures of reading prose fiction.

In "How Beautiful with Shoes" Steele uses the omniscient point of view at the beginning as he introduces the reader to the characters and the situation. In the opening paragraphs of the story we watch the action through the consciousness of various people. At the outset the point of view is Mare's: "Then in the quiet she heard a sound of hoofs on the bridge, where the road crossed the creek a hundred yards below the house, and she set the pail down on the ground beside her bare, barn-soiled feet." A little later, Mare leaves the scene and we are, for a brief moment, in the consciousness of the author: "For moments after the girl had disappeared beyond the willows the widow continued to call, unaware through long habit of how absurd it sounded, the name which that strange man her husband had put upon their daughter in one of his moods." Still later, we watch the action, briefly, through Ruby's eyes: "When he saw the girl getting over the fence under the willows he tongued the wad of tobacco out of his mouth into his palm, threw it away beyond the road, and drew a sleeve of his jumper across his lips." Once the conflict has started, however, Steele adheres strictly to the third-person point of view, letting the reader share Mare's experience by presenting all the action through Mare's consciousness: her two meetings with Jewett, the weird flight through the night, the final rescue at the hands of old man Wyker, the aftermath at her home. Steele shifts briefly to the omniscient point of view after the rescue as the neighbors gather at the Doggett home, but then once more returns to Mare's point of view and maintains it consistently until the end of the story.

## Plot

The basis of every story is a conflict between the central character and some opposing force, which lies either inside or outside him, or perhaps both. The conflict may be with another person or persons, or with his environment, or with some aspect of his own personality. Conflict arises from circumstances that cause an unstable situation (the origin of suspense) and is resolved when the character either overcomes this opposing force or succumbs to it, and the situation becomes stable again. What happens beyond that point is "another story."

Thus the plot of a story is, generally, a conflict and its resolution. Plot is intimately related to character and story idea, or theme; plot is, in fact, the inexorable working-out of the story in terms of the revealed traits of the characters. The emphasis is on causality; a story is a sequence of events in time. But events do not merely happen; they happen *because*—because a certain character with a specific moral nature and disposition, placed in a specific situation, is motivated to act in a certain way.

The elements of plot may be listed as exposition; point of attack; rising action, or complication; climax, or turning point; falling action; and dénouement. *Exposition* is the antecedent information necessary to understand the forward progress of the action; it includes a knowledge of the characters and their relation to each other, the time, the place, the situation out of which the conflict develops. In some stories very little exposition is necessary. Steele, for example, devotes little space to exposition in "How Beautiful with Shoes." Once the story is located for us in the New England countryside, the characters of Mare and Ruby clarified for us, and their engagement indicated, along with a quick picture of their casual love making, we are ready to move ahead with the action. In contrast to this, Sherwood Anderson devotes a good third of "I'm a Fool" to exposition, going into considerable detail about the character of his protagonist, the nineteen-year-old lad who is telling the story, and to earlier events in his life that bear on the present action. Much of this exposition is given in a *flashback*, the insertion of antecedent details after the action of the story has started, either by description or in a scene.

The *point of attack* is the place at which the conflict begins, where the *status quo* is disturbed. In Steele's story the point of attack comes with the escape of the homicidal "loony"; this is the event that disturbs the lives of Mare and Ruby, alters the even tenor of their way. The *rising action* consists of the incident or series of incidents by which the conflict is developed; and the *climax*, or turning point, is that point where we can see how the story must inevitably end (at least we can see this in retrospect). In Steele's story the rising action consists of Mare's two encounters with Humble Jewett, the abduction, the mad experience of that night, with the climax coming at the point where Jewett is shot and killed. The *falling action* is the movement from the climax to the *dénouement*, which is the solution, or "unknotting," of the conflict. Like most short stories, "How Beautiful with Shoes" has no falling action; we move directly from climax to dénouement. The dénouement, the aftermath, comes in the wake of the adventure as Mare sits in her room reliving the experience of the night before.

Few short stories, particularly contemporary ones, have such a fully developed plot pattern. Indeed, most of the time it is unrealistic to discuss the modern story in these terms. This is not to imply that the modern story has no plot. Wherever there is conflict and resolution, if only stalemate, there is plot. The best way to analyze the structure of a story is to note what the conflict is, what causes it, how it is resolved, and how it is worked out in terms of action.

## Action

Action is the physical movement of the characters in time, as well as what they think and what they say. Through action the plot is developed.

Action is presented in one of two ways: (1) by means of a *summary* or (2) by means of a *scene*. A summary, or *panorama* (as Percy Lubbock called it in *The Craft of Fiction*), is a narrative of events related in general terms, in which the reader is *told* what happened. A summary is capable of covering a good deal of ground and time in a few words and is often used as a link between scenes. For instance, in "How Beautiful with Shoes," Steele writes, at one point in the narrative: "Ruby went home, but Older Haskins stayed to supper with them, and helped Mare do the dishes afterward; it was nearly nine when he left." This is summary: we don't *see* what *takes* place; we are *told* what *took* place. Hours of time are covered in one sentence. Note, also, that we are kept at a distance from the characters; we are not close-up.

A *scene*, on the contrary, is an episode limited in time and place, with the action slowed down so that the reader can watch it take place in front of him. For instance, in the sentences that directly follow the summary sentence just quoted, Steele writes:

> The mother was already in bed, and Mare was about to sit down to get those shoes off her wretched feet at last, when she heard the cow carrying on up at the barn, lowing and kicking, and the next minute the sow was in it with a horning note. It might be a fox passing by to get at the henhouse or a weasel. Mare forgot her feet, took a broom-handle they used in boiling clothes, opened the back door, and stepped out. Blinking the lamplight from her eyes, she peered up toward the outbuildings, and saw the gable end of the barn standing like a red arrow in the dark, and the top of a butternut tree beyond it drawn in skeleton traceries, and just then a cock crowed.

This is the beginning of a scene that goes on for a number of pages. We watch Mare start to sit down, listen to the farm animals, conclude that they are perhaps being molested, pick up a broomhandle, go to the door, step outside, look toward the barn. All this action takes place in front of our eyes. Whereas the summary sentence covered several hours in twenty-five words, this portion of a scene covers several minutes in about one hundred and thirty-five words. Note, also, that we are close-up, watching the action as it happens.

## Setting

Stories do not take place in a void, but in a specific place at a specific time. This time and place constitute the setting, the background for the action. In "The Boarding House," by Joyce, the action takes place in Dublin shortly after the turn of the century. In "How Beautiful with Shoes" the action takes place in rural New England in the twenties. Polly's home in Dublin and Mare's in rural New England are worlds far-removed from each other. Physical surroundings, living conditions, customs, social milieu—all contribute to make the atmosphere of the two locales as different as night from day.

Setting, then, is the environment that surrounds the characters and influences them and their actions. It is the *total* environment, even including the physical objects associated with the characters. In Steele's story it includes the cows and the pigs in the barnyard of the Doggett farm, the clods of earth that Mare feels breaking between her bare toes, her bedroom off the kitchen in the farmhouse, the woods and the undergrowth on the hillside through which she struggles with Humble Jewett, the two-dollar shoes with cloth tops that hurt her feet. More than this, it is the atmosphere of the rural countryside that makes Mare's putting on her shoes an event in itself and that leads directly into the theme of the story.

Sometimes, the setting of a story is not important. There are stories in which the action is independent of any environment. But usually, it plays a distinct role in the action and contributes markedly to the total meaning. The heath in Thomas Hardy's novel *The Return of the Native* is as important as Eustacia Vye, who hates it, and Clym Yeobright, who loves it. It is a dominant factor in shaping the pattern of their lives, and Hardy makes this clear by devoting the initial chapter of the novel to the heath and its moods. Untamable, unchangeable, it remains as always, Hardy says, appealing to "a subtler and scarcer instinct, to a more recently learnt emotion, than that which responds to the sort of beauty called charming and fair."

## Story Idea (Theme)

A short story does more than merely present clearly defined characters acting in a particular environment, however interesting those characters may be, however absorbing their actions. Underlying the action, and controlling it, is always one idea, or theme, the unifying element that gives the story meaning. It is the author's commentary on life, his insight into the principles that govern human behavior. This is another way of saying that a short story is always *about* something, comes to some conclusion about life. And this is the governing factor in the author's selection of characters, the situation in which he places them, the actions he gives to them, and the very words in which he presents them.

This idea, or theme, is not necessarily a moral, such as "crime does not pay," or a message, "fortune favors the brave," although it may be; the story idea is an observation. If it poses a problem, that problem need not be solved, only observed. The theme may be specifically stated by the author, as in Katherine Anne Porter's "The Circus," or left to be inferred by the reader. But the theme is there all the time, illuminating and giving significance to all the details. If the story is well-written, the reader will find himself absorbed by the action, engrossed by the characters; but by the time he lays the story down, he should be aware of the author's vision of the world.

The grandmother in Miss Porter's story had qualms about allowing the children to attend the circus. When her son remarks that the children do not seem to be "much damaged" by the experience, she answers: "The fruits of their present are in a future so far off, neither of us may live to know whether harm has been done or not." In that remark lies the theme of the story, which governs every detail of character, plot, action, setting: Miranda's reactions to the crowd under the big tent, the noise, the flaring lights, the clowns, her leaving the circus in hysterics, her bursting into tears at the supper table, her waking up in the dark with nightmares, screaming in her sleep.

"How Beautiful with Shoes" is not merely the story of a farm girl, abducted by a dangerous lunatic, rescued and returned after a night of terror. The significance of the story resides in the theme that underlies the experience. Mare is betrothed to Ruby Herter, whose love-making, as we are shown at the outset, is casual and awkward and matter-of-fact. Steele makes a point of this, suggesting an almost animal relationship: "They were used to handling animals, both of them." Mare responds to Ruby with a passive mouth and a slow warmth, "formless, nameless, almost impersonal." Ruby's technique of showing Mare that she is his true love consists of yanking her head back by her braided hair, sticking his chin out pugnaciously, and blurting, "Listen, Mare, you wouldn't leave nobody else hug and kiss you, dang you!"

Humble Jewett, who abducts her, is bizarre and demented, but he races with her through a moonlit night in a world filled with loveliness that he makes her see. He holds her tenderly in his arms, breathes poetry into her ears: "Amarantha sweet and fair—Ah, braid no more that shining hair. . . . How beautiful are thy feet with shoes, O prince's daughter!" After she is restored to her home, all this comes back to Mare. Only then, Steele tells us, did the "conscious part of her brain begin to make words of the whispering," only then did she "smell the groundpine." And Mare begins to wonder, "Is it only crazy folks ever run like that and talk that way? . . . Is it only crazy folks ever say such things? . . . Or call you that?" With this experience, then, she awakens to the wonder and the beauty of love.

The immediate results of Mare's discovery are dramatic as she pushes Ruby out the door when he comes once more, wiping his mouth on his jumper sleeve and saying, "Come on, give us a kiss, babe!"

We can see in retrospect how everything in the story is aimed at bringing out Mare's awakened sensibilities; how theme is the governing factor for all the details. When the details click into place like this, then we can be sure that we have grasped the theme, know what the story is about.

Intimately related to the theme, and at times important in underlining it, are the symbols that an author uses.

## Symbolism

A symbol is something that stands for something else, over and above what it is in itself. For instance, a lily is a white flower, but it is also symbolic of purity; and since it blooms normally in the spring, it is associated with Easter and has acquired a religious connotation. The cross is a common religious symbol; the flag is a symbol of nationalism, love of country. Other symbols are less conventional but still easily understood, such as twilight, the approach of night, as a symbol of the end of life; the ocean as the restless ebb and flow of life itself. Still other symbols, such as those used by William Blake and William Butler Yeats and T. S. Eliot in their poetry, may be called "private" symbols, for they carry no such commonly accepted significance; and the reader must be initiated into their meaning, perhaps by the poet's expressed statement, in order to understand them.

Prose fiction, as well as poetry, makes use of symbols. In "Paul's Case" Willa Cather uses symbols to enforce her theme. Cordelia Street, where Paul lives, becomes the symbol of all that is ugly and commonplace. Note how often Cordelia Street is mentioned, how Paul "felt the waters close above his head" when he turned into Cordelia Street as he returned from the dream world of the concert hall. In New York, immersed in his dream world, he doubts the existence of Cordelia Street. Later, when reality closes in, "all the world had become Cordelia Street." Paul's red carnation is also symbolic; he wears it flauntingly in his buttonhole as he faces his teachers in his ordeal at school. The flower symbolizes all that Cordelia Street is not. And at the end of the story, he carefully buries the red carnations he is then wearing in the snow before he jumps in front of the train.

"The Rocking-Horse Winner" is symbolic throughout in its suggestion that society in its feverish search for money as a substitute for love is driving itself to destruction; for the story is surely more than a mere fantasy, a tale of supernatural powers in a young boy. The rocking horse itself is a symbol, in its furious mad rush, getting nowhere. Paul says that he does get where he wants to go, but it is all an illusion. Where he gets is the yawning gates of death, oblivion.

The selection and juxtaposition of concrete details in the mere description of a place can also have symbolic suggestion. Note the following passage:

The funeral procession had departed. We were alone. Before us lay a yellow mound of soggy clay, partly covered with huge wreaths of flowers and ferns. In front of the mound was the grave, cut clean and sheer to that wooden box five feet below. A fine, pattering rain splashed dirty yellow specks on the white blossoms of the lilies and the green of the ferns. It trickled along in the footprints on the edge of the grave, and finally fell, a yellow, sluggish stream, down into the grave itself.

Here the details of the soiling of the flowers (dirty specks on the white blossoms), the water trickling along in the footprints (someone was here, is now gone), and its final sluggish fall over the edge suggest the decay of the powers of the human body and its eventual descent into the grave.

But symbol hunting can be a dangerous habit, since there is no sure equation of object and symbolic significance. On the other hand, missing the symbols that the author used to enforce his theme could well mean missing half of what the author set out to convey. Reading "Bartleby the Scrivener" as nothing but the story of a curious clerk in a law office who was, perhaps, a psychopathic case is surely missing what Melville was saying. To read intelligently is to recognize everything that an author put into a story. It is also the refusal to read *into* a story something that the author did *not* put there.

## Style

With a discussion of style we come to the last of the techniques of prose fiction that contribute to the total meaning of a story. Style is the author's characteristic way of using language or the way he uses language in a particular story for a particular effect. A writer's style is the words he chooses, the images he selects, both literal and figurative, the sound of the word in the phrase, the rhythm and structure of his sentences. Style, in other words, is *how* a writer expresses himself over and above *what* he says.

"Style is the man himself," according to Count Georges Buffon (1707–1788). Certainly, the individuality of expression that marks one author from another is one of the things we mean by style. All mature writers of fiction have style in this sense, a characteristic mode of expression distinctively their own. Faulkner does not write like Hemingway, and Katherine Anne Porter does not write like Katherine Mansfield. Yet each is a craftsman in his own right, using language in his own way to gain certain effects.

Miss Mansfield was an immensely conscious craftsman, choosing sentence rhythm as carefully and deliberately as she chose words to portray her characters. About one of her stories, "Miss Brill," she said:

I chose not only the length of every sentence, but even the sound of every sentence. I chose the rise and fall of every paragraph to fit her, and to fit her on that day at that moment. After I'd written it I read it aloud—numbers of times—just as one would *play over* a musical composition, trying to get it nearer and nearer to the expression of Miss Brill, until it fitted her.

In "The Doll's House" note how she expresses Aunt Beryl's opinion of the smell of paint clinging to the doll's house in comparison with the children's:

[Aunt Beryl:] For, really, the smell of paint coming from that doll's house . . . was quite enough to make any one seriously ill, in Aunt Beryl's opinion. Even before the sacking was taken off. And when it was. . . .

[Children:] But perfect, perfect little house! Who could possibly mind the smell? It was part of the joy, part of the newness.

And when she speaks of the mother's permission to allow the girls at school to come, two at a time, to look at the doll's house, the prose sounds like a direct quotation: "Not to stay to tea, of course, or to come traipsing through the house. But just to stand quietly in the courtyard. . . ."

Hemingway, like Miss Mansfield, was painfully conscious of his style. He said that when he was young he wrote like Kipling, whom he admired, but that later on he knew he "had to break the language down and start new." In doing so, he developed a very distinct style, marked by the following: a simple sentence structure with a striking lack of subordinate elements; the piling-up of statement after statement, joined, if at all, with the conjunction "and"; the free use of concrete details, a vivid re-creation of the sense world; but few comparisons, few figures of speech, and those usually of the simplest sort; a heavy dependence upon dialogue, an excellent transcript of colloquial rhythms. Hemingway's style, widely imitated by writers of the hard-boiled school of fiction, effectively reflected the attitude toward life that one associates with him, the attitude of a spectator who looks and depicts, but refuses to comment. "The Killers" is typical Hemingway of the early period, its style devoid of ornament—simple, spare, elemental. In the opening the sentence structure is so primitive that it sounds almost like a first-grade reader:

> The door of Henry's lunchroom opened and two men came in. They sat down at the counter.
> "What's yours?" George asked them.
> "I don't know," one of the men said. "What do you want to eat, Al?"
> "I don't know," said Al. "I don't know what I want to eat."
> Outside it was getting dark. The street-light came on outside the window. The two men at the counter read the menu.

This is about as direct and elemental as expression can be. It is as though Hemingway were saying, "I'm giving it to you as straight and direct as I can. This is it."

Steele too is a superb craftsman whose sentences reflect any mood, intensify any emotion. Note the matter-of-fact quality of the following:

> Then in the quiet she heard a sound of hoofs on the bridge, where the road crossed the creek a hundred yards below the house, and she set the pail down on the ground beside her bare, barn-soiled feet. She picked it up again. She set it down. It was as if she calculated its weight.

Late in the story, when Mare is recalling what seems to her, in retrospect, the loveliness of the experience of the night before, Steele uses rhythms in his prose so close to poetry that it can almost be scanned:

Mare ran. She ran through a wind white with moonlight and wet with "the small rain." And the wind she ran through, it ran through her, and made her shiver as she ran. And the man beside her leaped high over the waves of the dead grasses and gathered the wind in his arms, and her hair was heavy and his was tossing, and a little fox ran before them across the top of the world. And the world spread down around in waves of black and silver, more immense than she had ever known the world could be, and more beautiful.

Style, then, is an aid to the meaning. It should, however, be unobtrusive. The most effective style is one that so fits the subject that the reader is unaware of it until he looks closely to see where the impact of the passage lies. It is like the background music to a first-rate motion picture, so much a part of the mood that it loses its own identity.

Let us look again at Steele's story, "How Beautiful with Shoes," to sum-marize what our examination of the various techniques of the short story has brought to light. Steele, we see, has written a story about a farm girl named Amarantha by her father, now dead, but who is called Mare by everyone except her deaf mother. The name Mare is symbolic; certainly, it fits her better than Amarantha. For she is large, slow-minded, inarticulate, close to the soil, skilled in handling animals, passive in her acceptance of things, rather phlegmatic in temperament. Her surname, Doggett, is also symbolic, suggest-ing the word "dogged."

The story is about her awakening to the wonder and beauty of love by way of a frightening, yet revealing, experience with an escaped homicidal lunatic, who developed a sudden attraction to her. This is the controlling idea, we see in retrospect. The lunatic's tender and poetic love-making turns him into a curious rival of her fiancé, Ruby Herter. He becomes a kind of foil for Ruby, whose own love-making displays itself in manifestations of aggressive masculinity.

Steele sets the story in New England, and opens it with a scene on the Doggett farm, which lies next door to that of Mare's fiancé. In this scene he characterizes both Mare and Ruby, and brings out the situation: they are betrothed; their love-making is casual and clumsy.

A complication enters their lives with the news that a homicidal lunatic, Humble Jewett, has escaped from a nearby asylum. This news leads at once to a physical separation between Mare and Ruby—Ruby immediately joins a posse engaged in hunting the lunatic down—a separation that will be more profound and significant before the story is over.

Action now begins with the appearance of the lunatic, who has eluded the pursuing posse and shows up at the Doggett farm. He is attracted to Mare by her name (he hears her deaf mother call her "Amarantha") and her yellow hair, both of which remind him of Lovelace's lines: "Amarantha, sweet and fair,/Ah, braid no more that shining hair." Mare is not the beauty that the lunatic, hypnotized by her name, declares her to be. But she shows her courage in leading him away from her mother into an open field, where he is captured by the returning posse.

This is the first stage of the action, and it accomplishes a number of things essential to the story: (1) Mare, temporizing with the lunatic, agrees that she loves him and will go away with him. This leads to his later return to the farm and to the abduction. (2) The aftermath of the capture, which brings a number of people to the farmhouse, brings about a natural revelation of information about the lunatic: he is college bred and taught in an academy before his mind gave way; thus his sensitivity to beauty and his love of poetry become clearly understandable. (3) The presence of Judge North and the later lingering of Older Haskins result in Mare's putting on her new shoes and leaving them on.

The second phase of the action is the abduction. Escaping from the jail after setting it on fire and killing the jailer, Jewett returns to the Doggett farm and makes off with Mare. The abduction is adequately motivated by the lunatic's attraction to Mare and her earlier forced declaration that she loves him and will go away with him. Ruby had joked about this: "Know the only thing they can get him to say, Mare? Only God thing he'll say is, 'Amarantha, she's goin' with me.' " Mare's presence on top of the rock pile, away from the house, is also logically accounted for in her natural desire to see more of the fire that drew her out of doors. So, also, is the lunatic's gentleness with her, in spite of the ever-present threat to her safety.

The action continues in a succession of scenes—the hiding from their pursuers; the mad dash through the countryside; the breaking into Wyker's cabin—scenes that hold us constantly in suspense, fraught as they are with the imminent possibility at all times that Mare will be raped or killed. Upon several occasions, with the lunatic's changing moods, one or the other seems near at hand. Ever present, also, is the strange love-making—the hand on the throat while the lips recite the poetry of Lovelace or the Song of Solomon; the strange tenderness and the beauty that she has never known; the gentle fingers caressing her hair; the hands softly exploring her body.

The climax comes with Mare's rescue by Wyker. A blast of a shotgun and Mare is returned to her home and her fiancé. The threat to the romance between her and Ruby is over. The *status quo* is restored. The lives of Mare and Ruby are back once more into their even groove.

But are they? Mare is physically unharmed. But she is not unchanged. In the aftermath of that frightful experience, she sits alone in her room recalling all that had happened. In retrospect, the terror drops away, and she remembers only the strange and wonderful love-making of her captor, which, in turn, makes her conscious of the shortcomings of Ruby, her fiancé, as a lover. This is brought home to us when Ruby, who is exactly the same as he was at the beginning of the story, wipes his mouth on his jumper sleeve as he had done only a few hours earlier and says, "Come on, give us a kiss, babe!" Before, she had yielded to him passively, "a slow warmth" pervading her. Her response now is to push him out the door crying, "Go 'way! Lea' me be!"

The story, of course, is Mare's story. She is the protagonist with whom we sympathize. And since the story deals with a discovery by Mare that changes her, Steele presents the story largely from her point of view. It is Mare's mind that we enter, Mare's feelings that we explore, Mare's reactions that we share. The conflict has been a significant one for the girl. She acts always within the bounds of her revealed character (as, indeed, do Ruby and Humble Jewett). And at the end of the story, the experience has left its mark on her. She will never be quite the same again, although she may get over her first revulsion for her fiancé.

Steele's style enhances the mounting tensions and suspense as vivid scenes depict the physical and emotional worlds through which Mare moves. Because both Mare and Humble Jewett's motivations are clear, there is a logical chain of cause and effect in the action. It is a bizarre story in some ways—a curious kind of love-making between an uneducated, phlegmatic, inarticulate girl and a demented, beauty-mad, former schoolteacher. But the characters are not mere freaks; they are made eminently understandable to us, and their story has universal significance that gives its theme validity.

WILBUR DANIEL STEELE

# ❧ How Beautiful with Shoes

By THE time the milking was finished, the sow, which had farrowed the past week, was making such a row that the girl spilled a pint of the warm milk down the trough-lead to quiet the animal before taking the pail to the well-house. Then in the quiet she heard a sound of hoofs on the bridge, where the road crossed the creek a hundred yards below the house, and she set the pail down on the ground beside her bare, barn-soiled feet. She picked it up again. She set it down. It was as if she calculated its weight.

That was what she was doing, as a matter of fact, setting off against its pull toward the well-house the pull of that wagon team in the road, with little more of personal will or wish in the matter than has a wooden weather-vane between two currents in the wind. And as with the vane, so with the wooden girl—the added behest of a whip-lash cracking in the distance was enough; leaving the pail at the barn door, she set off in a deliberate, docile beeline through the cow-yard, over the fence, and down in a diagonal across the farm's one tilled field toward the willow brake that walled the road at the dip. And once under way, though her mother came to the kitchen door and called in her high, flat voice, "Amarantha, where you goin', Amarantha?" the girl went on apparently unmoved, as though she had been as deaf as the woman in the doorway; indeed, if there was emotion in her it was the purely sensuous one of feeling the clods of the furrows breaking softly between her toes. It was springtime in the mountains.

"Amarantha, why don't you answer me, Amarantha?"

For moments after the girl had disappeared beyond the willows the widow continued to call, unaware through long habit of how absurd it sounded, the name which that strange man her husband had put upon their daughter in one of his moods. Mrs. Doggett had been deaf so long she did not realize that nobody else ever thought of it for the broad-fleshed, slow-minded girl, but called her Mary or, even more simply, Mare.

Ruby Herter had stopped his team this side of the bridge, the mules' heads turned into the lane to his father's farm beyond the road. A big-barreled, heavy-limbed fellow with a square, sallow, not unhandsome face, he took out youth in ponderous gestures of masterfulness; it was like him to have cracked his whip above his animals' ears the moment before he pulled them to a halt. When he saw the girl getting over the fence under the willows he tongued the wad of tobacco out of his mouth into his palm, threw it away beyond the road, and drew a sleeve of his jumper across his lips.

"Don't run yourself out o' breath, Mare; I got all night."

"I was comin'." It sounded sullen only because it was matter of fact.

"Well, keep a-comin' and give us a smack." Hunched on the wagon seat, he remained motionless for some time after she had arrived at the hub, and when he stirred it was but to cut a fresh bit of tobacco, as if already he had forgotten why he threw the old one away. Having satisfied his humor, he unbent, climbed down, kissed her passive mouth, and hugged her up to him, roughly and loosely, his hands careless of contours. It was not out of the way; they were used to handling animals, both of them; and it was spring. A slow warmth pervaded the girl, formless, nameless, almost impersonal.

Her betrothed pulled her head back by the braid of her yellow hair. He studied her face, his brows gathered and his chin out.

"Listen, Mare, you wouldn't leave nobody else hug and kiss you, dang you!"

She shook her head, without vehemence or anxiety.

"Who's that?" She hearkened up the road. "Pull your team out," she added, as a Ford came in sight around the bend above the house, driven at speed. "Geddap!" she said to the mules herself.

But the car came to a halt near them, and one of the five men crowded in it called, "Come on, Ruby, climb in. They's a loony loose out o' Dayville Asylum, and they got him trailed over somewheres on Split Ridge and Judge North phoned up to Slosson's store for ever'body come help circle him—come on, hop the runnin'-board!"

Ruby hesitated, an eye on his team.

"Scared, Ruby?" The driver raced his engine. "They say this boy's a killer."

"Mare, take the team in and tell pa." The car was already moving when Ruby jumped in. A moment after it had sounded on the bridge it was out of sight.

"Amarantha, Amarantha, why don't you come, Amarantha?"

Returning from her errand, fifteen minutes later, Mare heard the plaint lifted in the twilight. The sun had dipped behind the back ridge, and though the sky was still bright with day, the dusk began to smoke up out of the plowed field like a ground-fog. The girl had returned through it, got the milk, and started toward the well-house before the widow saw her.

"Daughter, seems to me you might!" she expostulated without change of key. "Here's some young man friend o' yourn stopped to say howdy, and I been rackin' my lungs out after you. . . . Put that milk in the cool and come!"

Some young man friend? But there was no good to be got from puzzling. Mare poured the milk in the pan in the dark of the low house over the well, and as she came out, stooping, she saw a figure waiting for her, black in silhouette against the yellowing sky.

"Who are you?" she asked, a native timidity making her sound sulky.

"Amarantha!" the fellow mused. "That's poetry." And she knew then that she did not know him.

She walked past, her arms straight down and her eyes front. Strangers always affected her with a kind of muscular terror simply by being strangers. So she gained the kitchen steps, aware by his tread that he followed. There, taking courage at sight of her mother in the doorway, she turned on him, her eyes at the level of his knees.

"Who are you and what d' y' want?"

He still mused. "Amarantha! Amarantha in Carolina! That makes me happy!"

Mare hazarded one upward look. She saw that he had red hair, brown eyes, and hollows under his cheekbones, and though the green sweater he wore on top of a gray overall was plainly not meant for him, sizes too large as far as girth went, yet he was built so long of limb that his wrists came inches out of the sleeves and made his big hands look even bigger.

Mrs. Doggett complained. "Why don't you introduce us, daughter?"

The girl opened her mouth and closed it again. Her mother, unaware that no sound had come out of it, smiled and nodded, evidently taking to the tall, homely fellow and tickled by the way he could not seem to get his eyes off her daughter. But the daughter saw none of it, all her attention centered upon the stranger's hands.

Restless, hard-fleshed, and chap-bitten, they were like a countryman's hands; but the fingers were longer than the ordinary, and slightly spatulate at their ends, and these ends were slowly and continuously at play among themselves.

The girl could not have explained how it came to her to be frightened and at the same time to be calm, for she was inept with words. It was simply that in an animal way she knew animals, knew them in health and ailing, and when they were ailing she knew by instinct, as her father had known, how to move so as not to fret them.

Her mother had gone in to light up; from beside the lampshelf she called back, "If he's aimin' to stay to supper you should've told me, Amarantha, though I guess there's plenty of the side-meat to go 'round, if you'll bring me in a few more turnips and potatoes, though it is late."

At the words the man's cheeks moved in and out. "I'm very hungry," he said.

Mare nodded deliberately. Deliberately, as if her mother could hear her, she said over her shoulder, "I'll go get the potatoes and turnips, ma." While she spoke she was moving, slowly, softly, at first, toward the right of the yard, where the fence gave over into the field. Unluckily her mother spied her through the window.

"Amarantha, where *are* you goin'?"

"I'm goin' to get the potatoes and turnips." She neither raised her voice nor glanced back, but lengthened her stride. "He won't hurt her," she said to herself. "He won't hurt her; it's me, not her," she kept repeating, while she got over the fence and down into the shadow that lay more than ever like a fog on the field.

The desire to believe that it actually did hide her, the temptation to break from her rapid but orderly walk grew till she could no longer fight it. She saw the road willows only a dash ahead of her. She ran, her feet floundering among the furrows.

She neither heard nor saw him, but when she realized he was with her she knew he had been with her all the while. She stopped, and he stopped, and so they stood, with the dark open of the field all around. Glancing sidewise presently, she saw he was no longer looking at her with those strangely importunate brown eyes of his, but had raised them to the crest of the wooded ridge behind her.

By and by, "What does it make you think of?" he asked. And when she made no move to see, "Turn around and look!" he said, and though it was low and almost tender in its tone, she knew enough to turn.

A ray of the sunset hidden in the west struck through the tops of the topmost trees, far and small up there, a thin, bright hem.

"What does it make you think of, Amarantha? . . . Answer!"

"Fire," she made herself say.

"Or blood."

"Or blood, yeh. That's right, or blood." She had heard a Ford going up the road beyond the willows, and her attention was not on what she said.

The man soliloquized. "Fire and blood, both; spare one or the other, and where is beauty, the way the world is? It's an awful thing to have to carry, but Christ had it. Christ came with a sword. I love beauty, Amarantha. . . . I say, I love beauty!"

"Yeh, that's right, I hear." What she heard was the car stopping at the house.

"Not prettiness. Prettiness'll have to go with ugliness, because it's only ugliness trigged up. But beauty!" Now again he was looking at her. "Do you know how beautiful you are, Amarantha, 'Amarantha sweet and fair'?" Of a sudden, reaching behind her, he began to unravel the meshes of her hair-braid, the long, flat-tipped fingers at once impatient and infinitely gentle. " 'Braid no more that shining hair!' "

Flat-faced Mare Doggett tried to see around those glowing eyes so near to hers, but wise in her instinct, did not try too hard. "Yeh," she temporized. "I mean, no, I mean."

"Amarantha, I've come a long, long way for you. Will you come away with me now?"

"Yeh—that is—in a minute I will, mister—yeh . . ."

"Because you want to, Amarantha? Because you love me as I love you? Answer!"

"Yeh—sure—uh . . . *Ruby!*"

The man tried to run, but there were six against him, coming up out of the dark that lay in the plowed ground. Mare stood where she was while they knocked him down and got a rope around him; after that she walked back toward the house with Ruby and Older Haskins, her father's cousin.

Ruby wiped his brow and felt of his muscles. "Gees, you're lucky we come, Mare. We're no more'n past the town, when they come hollerin' he'd broke over this way."

When they came to the fence the girl sat on the rail for a moment and rebraided her hair before she went into the house, where they were making her mother smell ammonia.

Lots of cars were coming. Judge North was coming, somebody said. When Mare heard this she went into her bedroom off the kitchen and got her shoes and put them on. They were brand new two-dollar shoes with cloth tops, and she had only begun to break them in last Sunday; she wished afterwards she had put her stockings on too, for they would have eased the seams. Or else that she had put on the old button pair, even though the soles were worn through.

Judge North arrived. He thought first of taking the loony straight through to Dayville that night, but then decided to keep him in the lock-up at the courthouse till morning and make the drive by day. Older Haskins stayed in, gentling Mrs. Doggett, while Ruby went out to help get the man into the Judge's sedan. Now that she had them on, Mare didn't like to take the shoes off till Older went; it might make him feel small, she thought.

Older Haskins had a lot of facts about the loony.

"His name's Humble Jewett," he told them. "They belong back in Breed County, all them Jewetts, and I don't reckon there's none of 'em that's not a mite unbalanced. He went to college though, worked his way, and he taught somethin' 'rother in some academy-school a spell, till he went off his head all of a sudden and took after folks with an axe. I remember it in the paper at the time. They give out one while how the Principal wasn't goin' to live, and there was others—there was a girl he tried to strangle. That was four—five year back."

Ruby came in guffawing. "Know the only thing they can get 'im to say, Mare? Only God thing he'll say is, 'Amarantha, she's goin' with me.' . . . Mare!"

"Yeh, I know."

The cover of the kettle the girl was handling slid off the stove with a clatter. A sudden sick wave passed over her. She went out to the back, out into the air. It was not till now she knew how frightened she had been.

Ruby went home, but Older Haskins stayed to supper with them, and helped Mare do the dishes afterward; it was nearly nine when he left. The mother was already in bed, and Mare was about to sit down to get those shoes off her wretched feet at last, when she heard the cow carrying on up at the barn, lowing and kicking, and next minute the sow was in it with a horning note. It might be a fox passing by to get at the hen-house, or a weasel. Mare forgot her feet, took a broom-handle they used in boiling clothes, opened the back door, and stepped out. Blinking the lamplight from her eyes, she peered up toward the outbuildings, and saw the gable end of the barn standing like a red arrow in the dark, and the top of a butternut tree beyond it drawn in skeleton traceries, and just then a cock crowed.

She went to the right corner of the house and saw where the light came from, ruddy above the woods down the valley. Returning into the house, she bent close to her mother's ear and shouted, "Somethin's a-fire down to the town, looks like," then went out again and up to the barn. "Soh! Soh!" she called to the animals. She climbed up and stood on the top rail of the cow-pen fence, only to find she could not locate the flame even there.

Ten rods behind the buildings a mass of rock mounted higher than their ridgepoles, a chopped-off buttress of the back ridge, covered with oak scrub and wild grapes and blackberries, whose thorny ropes the girl beat away from her skirt with the broom-handle as she scrambled up in the wine-colored dark. Once at the top, and the brush held aside, she could see the tongue-tip of the conflagration half a mile away at the town. And she knew by the bearing of the two church steeples that it was the building where the lock-up was that was burning.

There is a horror in knowing animals trapped in a fire, no matter what the animals.

"Oh, my God!" Mare said.

A car went down the road. Then there was a horse galloping. That would be Older Haskins probably. People were out at Ruby's father's farm; she could hear their voices raised. There must have been another car up from the other way, for lights wheeled and shouts were exchanged in the neighborhood of the bridge. Next thing she knew, Ruby was at the house below, looking for her probably.

He was telling her mother. Mrs. Doggett was not used to him, so he had to shout even louder than Mare had to.

"What y' reckon he done, the hellion! he broke the door and killed Lew Fyke and set the courthouse afire! . . . Where's Mare?"

Her mother would not know. Mare called. "Here, up the rock here."

She had better go down. Ruby would likely break his bones if he tried to climb the rock in the dark, not knowing the way. But the sight of the fire fascinated her simple spirit, the fearful element, more fearful than ever now, with the news. "Yes, I'm comin'," she called sulkily, hearing feet in the brush. "You wait; I'm comin'."

When she turned and saw it was Humble Jewett, right behind her among the branches, she opened her mouth to screech. She was not quick enough. Before a sound came out he got one hand over her face and the other arm around her body.

Mare had always thought she was strong, and the loony looked gangling, yet she was so easy for him that he need not hurt her. He made no haste and little noise as he carried her deeper into the undergrowth. Where the hill began to mount it was harder though. Presently he set her on her feet. He let the hand that had been over her mouth slip down to her throat, where the broad-tipped fingers wound, tender as yearning, weightless as caress.

"I was afraid you'd scream before you knew who 'twas, Amarantha. But I didn't want to hurt your lips, dear heart, your lovely, quiet lips."

It was so dark under the trees she could hardly see him, but she felt his breath on her mouth, near to. But then, instead of kissing her, he said, "No! No!" took from her throat for an instant the hand that had held her mouth, kissed its palm, and put it back softly against her skin.

"Now, my love, let's go before they come."

She stood stock still. Her mother's voice was to be heard in the distance, strident and meaningless. More cars were on the road. Nearer, around the rock, there were sounds of tramping and thrashing. Ruby fussed and cursed. He shouted, "Mare, dang you, where are you, Mare?" his voice harsh with uneasy anger. Now, if she aimed to do anything, was the time to do it. But there was neither breath nor power in her windpipe. It was as if those yearning fingers had paralyzed the muscles.

"Come!" The arm he put around her shivered against her shoulder blades. It was anger. "I hate killing. It's a dirty, ugly thing. It makes me sick." He gagged, judging by the sound. But then he ground his teeth. "Come away, my love!"

She found herself moving. Once when she broke a branch underfoot with an instinctive awkwardness he chided her. "Quiet, my heart, else they'll hear!" She made herself heavy. He thought she grew tired and bore more of her weight till he was breathing hard.

Men came up the hill. There must have been a dozen spread out, by the angle of their voices as they kept touch. Always Humble Jewett kept caressing Mare's throat with one hand; all she could do was hang back.

"You're tired and you're frightened," he said at last. "Get down here."

There were twigs in the dark, the overhang of a thicket of some sort. He thrust her in under this, and lay beside her on the bed of groundpine. The hand that was not in love with her throat reached across her; she felt the weight of its forearm on her shoulder and its fingers among the strands of her hair, eagerly, but tenderly, busy. Not once did he stop speaking, no louder than breathing, his lips to her ear.

"'Amarantha sweet and fair—Ah, braid no more that shining hair . . .'"

Mare had never heard of Lovelace, the poet; she thought the loony was just going on, hardly listened, got little sense. But the cadence of it added to the lethargy of all her flesh.

"'Like a clew of golden thread—Most excellently ravelléd . . .'"

Voices loudened; feet came tramping; a pair went past not two rods away.

"'. . . Do not then wind up the light—In ribbands, and o'ercloud in night . . .'"

The search went on up the woods, men shouting to one another and beating the brush.

" '. . . *But shake your head and scatter day!*' I've never loved, Amarantha. They've tried me with prettiness, but prettiness is too cheap, yes, it's too cheap."

Mare was cold, and the coldness made her lazy. All she knew was that he talked on.

"But dogwood blowing in the spring isn't cheap. The earth of a field isn't cheap. Lots of time I've laid down and kissed the earth of a field, Amarantha. That's beauty, and a kiss for beauty." His breath moved up her cheek. He trembled violently. "No, no, not yet!" He got to his knees and pulled her by an arm. "We can go now."

They went back down the slope, but at an angle, so that when they came to the level they passed two hundred yards to the north of the house, and crossed the road there. More and more, her walking was like sleepwalking, the feet numb in their shoes. Even where he had to let go of her, crossing the creek on stones, she stepped where he stepped with an obtuse docility. The voices of the searchers on the back ridge were small in distance when they began to climb the face of Coward Hill, on the opposite side of the valley.

There is an old farm on top of Coward Hill, big hayfields as flat as tables. It had been half-past nine when Mare stood on the rock above the barn; it was toward midnight when Humble Jewett put aside the last branches of the woods and let her out on the height, and half a moon had risen. And a wind blew there, tossing the withered tops of last year's grasses, and mists ran with the wind, and ragged shadows with the mists, and mares'-tails of clear moonlight among the shadows, so that now the boles of birches on the forest's edge beyond the fences were but opal blurs and now cut alabaster. It struck so cold against the girl's cold flesh, this wind, that another wind of shivers blew through her, and she put her hands over her face and eyes. But the madman stood with his eyes wide open and his mouth open, drinking the moonlight and the wet wind.

His voice, when he spoke at last, was thick in his throat.

"Get down on your knees." He got down on his and pulled her after. "And pray!"

Once in England a poet sang four lines. Four hundred years have forgotten his name, but they have remembered his lines. The daft man knelt upright, his face raised to the wild scud, his long wrists hanging to the dead grass. He began simply:

> " 'O western wind, when wilt thou blow
> That the small rain down can rain?' "

The Adam's-apple was big in his bent throat. As simply he finished.

> " 'Christ, that my love were in my arms
> And I in my bed again!' "

Mare got up and ran. She ran without aim or feeling in the power of the wind. She told herself again that the mists would hide her from him, as she had done at dusk. And again, seeing that he ran at her shoulder, she knew he had been there all the while, making a race of it, flailing the air with his long arms for joy of play in the cloud of spring, throwing his knees high, leaping the moon-blue waves of the brown grass, shaking his bright hair; and her own hair was a weight behind her, lying level on the wind. Once a shape went bounding ahead of them for instants; she did not realize it was a fox till it was gone.

She never thought of stopping; she never thought anything, except once, "Oh, my God, I wish I had my shoes off!" And what would have been the good in stopping or in turning another way, when it was only play? The man's ecstasy magnified his strength. When a snake-fence came at them he took the top rail in flight, like a college hurdler, and, seeing the girl hesitate and half turn as if to flee, he would have releaped it without touching a hand. But then she got a loom of buildings, climbed over quickly, before he should jump, and ran along the lane that ran with the fence.

Mare had never been up there, but she knew that the farm and the house belonged to a man named Wyker, a kind of cousin of Ruby Herter's, a violent, bearded old fellow who lived by himself. She could not believe her luck. When she had run half the distance and Jewett had not grabbed her, doubt grabbed her instead. "Oh, my God, go careful!" she told herself. "Go slow!" she implored herself, and stopped running, to walk.

Here was a misgiving the deeper in that it touched her special knowledge. She had never known an animal so far gone that its instincts failed it; a starving rat will scent the trap sooner than a fed one. Yet, after one glance at the house they approached, Jewett paid it no further attention, but walked with his eyes to the right, where the cloud had blown away, and wooded ridges, like black waves rimmed with silver, ran down away toward the Valley of Virginia.

"I've never lived!" In his single cry there were two things, beatitude and pain.

Between the bigness of the falling world and his eyes the flag of her hair blew. He reached out and let it whip between his fingers. Mare was afraid it would break the spell then, and he would stop looking away and look at the house again. So she did something almost incredible; she spoke.

"It's a pretty—I mean—a beautiful view down that-away."

"God Almighty beautiful, to take your breath away. I knew I'd never loved, Belovéd—" He caught a foot under the long end of one of the boards that covered the well and went down heavily on his hands and knees. It seemed to make no difference. "But I never knew I'd never lived," he finished in the same tone of strong rapture, quadruped in the grass, while Mare ran for the door and grabbed the latch.

When the latch would not give, she lost what little sense she had. She pounded with her fists. She cried with all her might: "Oh—hey—in there—hey—in there!" Then Jewett came and took her gently between his hands and drew her away, and then, though she was free, she stood in something like an awful embarrassment while he tried shouting.

"Hey! Friend! whoever you are, wake up and let my love and me come in!"

"No!" wailed the girl.

He grew peremptory. "Hey, wake up!" He tried the latch. He passed to full fury in a wink's time; he cursed, he kicked, he beat the door till Mare thought he would break his hands. Withdrawing, he ran at it with his shoulder; it burst at the latch, went slamming in, and left a black emptiness. His anger dissolved in a big laugh. Turning in time to catch her by a wrist, he cried joyously, "Come, my Sweet One!"

"No! No! Please—aw—listen. There ain't nobody there. He ain't to home. It wouldn't be right to go in anybody's house if they wasn't to home, you know that."

His laugh was blither than ever. He caught her high in his arms.

"I'd do the same by his love and him if 'twas my house, I would." At the threshold he paused and thought, "That is, if she was the true love of his heart forever."

The room was the parlor. Moonlight slanted in at the door, and another shaft came through a window and fell across a sofa, its covering dilapidated, showing its wadding in places. The air was sour, but both of them were farm-bred.

"Don't, Amarantha!" His words were pleading in her ear. "Don't be so frightened."

He set her down on the sofa. As his hands let go of her they were shaking.

"But look, I'm frightened too." He knelt on the floor before her, reached out his hands, withdrew them. "See, I'm afraid to touch you." He mused, his eyes rounded. "Of all the ugly things there are, fear is the ugliest. And yet, see, it can be the very beautifulest. That's a strange queer thing."

The wind blew in and out of the room, bringing the thin, little bitter sweetness of new April at night. The moonlight that came across Mare's shoulders fell full upon his face, but hers it left dark, ringed by the aureole of her disordered hair.

"Why do you wear a halo, Love?" He thought about it. "Because you're an angel, is that why?" The swift, untempered logic of the mad led him to dismay. His hands came flying to hers, to make sure they were of earth; and he touched her breast, her shoulders, and her hair. Peace returned to his eyes as his fingers twined among the strands.

" *Thy hair is as a flock of goats that appear from Gilead . . .* " He spoke like a man dreaming. " *Thy temples are like a piece of pomegranate within thy locks.* "

Mare never knew that he could not see her for the moonlight.

"Do you remember, Love?"

She dared not shake her head under his hand. "Yeh, I reckon," she temporized.

"You remember how I sat at your feet, long ago, like this, and made up a song? And all the poets in all the world have never made one to touch it, have they, Love?"

"Ugh-ugh—never."

" 'How beautiful are thy feet with shoes . . .' Remember?"

"Oh, my God, what's he sayin' now?" she wailed to herself.

" 'How beautiful are thy feet with shoes, O prince's daughter! the joints of thy thighs are like jewels, the work of the hands of a cunning workman.

Thy navel is like a round goblet, which wanteth not liquor; thy belly is like an heap of wheat set about with lilies.
Thy two breasts are like two young roes that are twins.' "

Mare had not been to church since she was a little girl, when her mother's black dress wore out. "No, no!" she wailed under her breath. "You're awful to say such awful things." She might have shouted it; nothing could have shaken the man now, rapt in the immortal, passionate periods of Solomon's song.

" '. . . now also thy breasts shall be as clusters of the vine, and the smell of thy nose like apples.' "

Hotness touched Mare's face for the first time. "Aw, no, don't talk so!"

" 'And the roof of thy mouth like the best wine for my belovéd . . . causing the lips of them that are asleep to speak.' "

He had ended. His expression changed. Ecstasy gave place to anger, love to hate. And Mare felt the change in the weight of the fingers in her hair.

"What do you mean, I mustn't say it like that?" But it was not to her his fury spoke, for he answered himself straightway. "Like poetry, Mr. Jewett; I won't have blasphemy around my school."

"Poetry! My God! if that isn't poetry—if that isn't music—" . . . "It's Bible, Jewett. What you're paid to teach here is literature."

"Doctor Ryeworth, you're the blasphemer and you're an ignorant man." . . . "And your Principal. And I won't have you going around reading sacred allegory like earthly love."

"Ryeworth, you're an old man, a dull man, a dirty man, and you'd be better dead."

Jewett's hand had slid down from Mare's head. "Then I went to put my fingers around his throat, so. But my stomach turned, and I didn't do it. I went to my room. I laughed all the way to my room. I sat in my room at my table and I laughed. I laughed all afternoon and long after dark came. And then, about ten, somebody came and stood beside me in my room."

" 'Wherefore dost thou laugh, son?'

"Then I knew who He was, He was Christ.

" 'I was laughing about that dirty, ignorant, crazy old fool, Lord.'

" 'Wherefore dost thou laugh?'

"I didn't laugh any more. He didn't say any more. I kneeled down, bowed my head.

" 'Thy will be done! Where is he, Lord?'

" 'Over at the girls' dormitory, waiting for Blossom Sinckley.'

"Brassy Blossom, dirty Blossom . . ."

It had come so suddenly it was nearly too late. Mare tore at his hands with hers, tried with all her strength to pull her neck away.

"Filthy Blossom! and him an old filthy man, Blossom! and you'll find him in Hell when you reach there, Blossom . . ."

It was more the nearness of his face than the hurt of his hands that gave her power of fright to choke out three words.

"*I—ain't—Blossom!*"

Light ran in crooked veins. Through the veins she saw his face bewildered. His hands loosened. One fell down and hung; the other he lifted and put over his eyes, took away again and looked at ner.

"Amarantha!" His remorse was fearful to see. "What have I done!" His hands returned to hover over the hurts, ravening with pity, grief and tenderness. Tears fell down his cheeks. And with that, dammed desire broke its dam.

"Amarantha, my love, my dove, my beautiful love—"

"*And I ain't Amarantha neither, I'm Mary! Mary, that's my name!*"

She had no notion what she had done. He was like a crystal crucible that a chemist watches, changing hue in a wink with one adeptly added drop; but hers was not the chemist's eye. All she knew was that she felt light and free of him; all she could see of his face as he stood away above the moonlight were the whites of his eyes.

"Mary!" he muttered. A slight paroxysm shook his frame. So in the transparent crucible desire changed its hue. He retreated farther, stood in the dark by some tall piece of furniture. And still she could see the whites of his eyes.

"Mary! Mary Adorable!" A wonder was in him. "Mother of God!"

Mare held her breath. She eyed the door, but it was too far. And already he came back to go on his knees before her, his shoulders so bowed and his face so lifted that it must have cracked his neck, she thought; all she could see on the face was pain.

"Mary Mother, I'm sick to my death. I'm so tired."

She had seen a dog like that, one she had loosed from a trap after it had been there three days, its caught leg half gnawed free. Something about the eyes.

"Mary Mother, take me in your arms . . ."

Once again her muscles tightened. But he made no move.

". . . and give me sleep."

No, they were worse than the dog's eyes.

"Sleep, sleep! why won't they let me sleep? Haven't I done it all yet,

Mother? Haven't I washed them yet of all their sins? I've drunk the cup that was given me; is there another? They've mocked me and reviled me, broken my brow with thorns and my hands with nails, and I've forgiven them, for they knew not what they did. Can't I go to sleep now, Mother?"

Mare could not have said why, but now she was more frightened than she had ever been. Her hands lay heavy on her knees, side by side, and she could not take them away when he bowed his head and rested his face upon them.

After a moment he said one thing more. "Take me down gently when you take me from the Tree."

Gradually the weight of his body came against her shins, and he slept.

The moon streak that entered by the eastern window crept north across the floor, thinner and thinner; the one that fell through the southern doorway traveled east and grew fat. For a while Mare's feet pained her terribly and her legs too. She dared not move them, though, and by and by they did not hurt so much.

A dozen times, moving her head slowly on her neck, she canvassed the shadows of the room for a weapon. Each time her eyes came back to a heavy earthenware pitcher on a stand some feet to the left of the sofa. It would have had flowers in it when Wyker's wife was alive; probably it had not been moved from its dust-ring since she died. It would be a long grab, perhaps too long; still, it might be done if she had her hands.

To get her hands from under the sleeper's head was the task she set herself. She pulled first one, then the other, infinitesimally. She waited. Again she tugged a very, very little. The order of his breathing was not disturbed. But at the third trial he stirred.

"Gently! gently!" His own muttering waked him more. With some drowsy instinct of possession he threw one hand across her wrists, pinning them together between thumb and fingers. She kept dead quiet, shut her eyes, lengthened her breathing, as if she too slept.

There came a time when what was pretense grew to be a peril; strange as it was, she had to fight to keep her eyes open. She never knew whether or not she really napped. But something changed in the air, and she was wide awake again. The moonlight was fading on the doorsill, and the light that runs before dawn waxed in the window behind her head.

And then she heard a voice in the distance, lifted in maundering song. It was old man Wyker coming home after a night, and it was plain he had had some whisky.

Now a new terror laid hold of Mare.

"Shut up, you fool you!" she wanted to shout. "Come quiet, quiet!" She might have chanced it now to throw the sleeper away from her and scramble and run, had his powers of strength and quickness not taken her simple imagination utterly in thrall.

Happily the singing stopped. What had occurred was that the farmer had espied the open door and, even befuddled as he was, wanted to know more about it quietly. He was so quiet that Mare began to fear he had gone away. He had the squirrel-hunter's foot, and the first she knew of him was when she looked and saw his head in the doorway, his hard, soiled, whiskery face half-up-side-down with craning.

He had been to the town. Between drinks he had wandered in and out of the night's excitement; had even gone a short distance with one search party himself. Now he took in the situation in the room. He used his forefinger. First he held it to his lips. Next he pointed it with a jabbing motion at the sleeper. Then he tapped his own forehead and described wheels. Lastly, with his whole hand, he made pushing gestures, for Mare to wait. Then he vanished as silently as he had appeared.

The minutes dragged. The light in the east strengthened and turned rosy. Once she thought she heard a board creaking in another part of the house, and looked down sharply to see if the loony stirred. All she could see of his face was a temple with freckles on it and the sharp ridge of a cheekbone, but even from so little she knew how deeply and peacefully he slept. The door darkened. Wyker was there again. In one hand he carried something heavy; with the other he beckoned.

"Come jumpin'!" he said out loud.

Mare went jumping, but her cramped legs threw her down half way to the sill; the rest of the distance she rolled and crawled. Just as she tumbled through the door it seemed as if the world had come to an end above her; two barrels of a shotgun discharged into a room make a noise. Afterwards all she could hear in there was something twisting and bumping on the floor-boards. She got up and ran.

Mare's mother had gone to pieces; neighbor women put her to bed when Mare came home. They wanted to put Mare to bed, but she would not let them. She sat on the edge of her bed in her lean-to bedroom off the kitchen, just as she was, her hair down all over her shoulders and her shoes on, and stared away from them, at a place in the wallpaper.

"Yeh, I'll go myself. Lea' me be!"

The women exchanged quick glances, thinned their lips, and left her be. "God knows," was all they would answer to the questionings of those that had not gone in, "but she's gettin' herself to bed."

When the doctor came through he found her sitting just as she had been, still dressed, her hair down on her shoulders and her shoes on.

"What d' y' want?" she muttered and stared at the place in the wallpaper.

How could Doc Paradise say, when he did not know himself?

"I didn't know if you might be—might be feeling very smart, Mary."

"I'm all right. Lea' me be."

It was a heavy responsibility. Doc shouldered it. "No, it's all right," he said to the men in the road. Ruby Herter stood a little apart, chewing sullenly and looking another way. Doc raised his voice to make certain it carried. "Nope, nothing."

Ruby's ears got red, and he clamped his jaws. He knew he ought to go in and see Mare, but he was not going to do it while everybody hung around waiting to see if he would. A mule tied near him reached out and mouthed his sleeve in idle innocence; he wheeled and banged a fist against the side of the animal's head.

"Well, what d' y' aim to do 'bout it?" he challenged its owner.

He looked at the sun then. It was ten in the morning. "Hell, I got work!" he flared, and set off down the road for home. Doc looked at Judge North, and the Judge started after Ruby. But Ruby shook his head angrily. "Lea' me be!" He went on, and the Judge came back.

It got to be eleven and then noon. People began to say, "Like enough she'd be as thankful if the whole neighborhood wasn't camped here." But none went away.

As a matter of fact they were no bother to the girl. She never saw them. The only move she made was to bend her ankles over and rest her feet on edge; her shoes hurt terribly and her feet knew it, though she did not. She sat all the while staring at that one figure in the wallpaper, and she never saw the figure.

Strange as the night had been, this day was stranger. Fright and physical pain are perishable things once they are gone. But while pain merely dulls and telescopes in memory and remains diluted pain, terror looked back upon has nothing of terror left. A gambling chance taken, at no matter what odds, and won was a sure thing since the world's beginning; perils come through safely were never perilous. But what fright does do in retrospect is this—it heightens each sensuous recollection, like a hard, clear lacquer laid on wood, bringing out the color and grain of it vividly.

Last night Mare had lain stupid with fear on groundpine beneath a bush, loud foot-falls and light whispers confused in her ear. Only now, in her room, did she smell the groundpine.

Only now did the conscious part of her brain begin to make words of the whispering.

"*Amarantha*," she remembered, "*Amarantha sweet and fair*." That was as far as she could go for the moment, except that the rhyme with "fair" was "hair." But then a puzzle, held in abeyance, brought other words. She wondered what "ravel Ed" could mean. "*Most excellently ravellèd*." It was left to her mother to bring the end.

They gave up trying to keep her mother out at last. The poor woman's prostration took the form of fussiness.

"Good gracious, daughter, you look a sight. Them new shoes, half ruined; ain't your feet *dead?* And look at your hair, all tangled like a wild one!"

She got a comb.

"Be quiet, daughter; what's ailin' you. Don't shake your head!"

" '*But shake your head and scatter day.*' "

"What you say, Amarantha?" Mrs. Doggett held an ear down.

"Go 'way! Lea' me be!"

Her mother was hurt and left. And Mare ran, as she stared at the wallpaper. *"Christ, that my love were in my arms . . ."*

Mare ran. She ran through a wind white with moonlight and wet with "the small rain." And the wind she ran through, it ran through her, and made her shiver as she ran. And the man beside her leaped high over the waves of the dead grasses and gathered the wind in his arms, and her hair was heavy and his was tossing, and a little fox ran before them across the top of the world. And the world spread down around in waves of black and silver, more immense than she had ever known the world could be, and more beautiful.

*"God Almighty beautiful, to take your breath away!"*

Mare wondered, and she was not used to wondering. "Is it only crazy folks ever run like that and talk that way?"

She no longer ran; she walked; for her breath was gone. And there was some other reason, some other reason. Oh, yes, it was because her feet were hurting her. So, at last, and roundabout, her shoes had made contact with her brain.

Bending over the side of the bed, she loosened one of them mechanically. She pulled it half off. But then she looked down at it sharply, and she pulled it on again.

*"How beautiful . . ."*

Color overspread her face in a slow wave.

*"How beautiful are thy feet with shoes . . ."*

"Is it only crazy folks ever say such things?"

*"O prince's daughter!"*

"Or call you that?"

By and by there was a knock at the door. It opened, and Ruby Herter came in.

"Hello, Mare old girl!" His face was red. He scowled and kicked at the floor. "I'd 'a' been over sooner, except we got a mule down sick." He looked at his dumb betrothed. "Come on, cheer up, forget it! He won't scare you no more, not that boy, not what's left o' him. What you lookin' at, sourface? Ain't you glad to see me?"

Mare quit looking at the wallpaper and looked at the floor.

"Yeh," she said.

"That's more like it, babe." He came and sat beside her; reached down behind her and gave her a spank. "Come on, give us a kiss, babe!" He wiped his mouth on his jumper sleeve, a good farmer's sleeve, spotted with milking. He put his hands on her; he was used to handling animals. "Hey, you, warm up a little, reckon I'm goin' to do all the lovin'?"

"Ruby, lea' me be!"

"What!"

She was up, twisting. He was up, purple.

"What's ailin' you, Mare? What you bawlin' about?"

"Nothin'—only go 'way!"

She pushed him to the door and through it with all her strength, and closed it in his face, and stood with her weight against it, crying, "Go 'way! Go 'way! Lea' me be!"

# ❧ *I'm a Fool*

It was a hard jolt for me, one of the most bitterest I ever had to face. And it all came about through my own foolishness too. Even yet, sometimes, when I think of it, I want to cry or swear or kick myself. Perhaps, even now, after all this time, there will be a kind of satisfaction in making myself look cheap by telling of it.

It began at three o'clock one October afternoon as I sat in the grandstand at the fall trotting and pacing meet at Sandusky, Ohio.

To tell the truth, I felt a little foolish that I should be sitting in the grandstand at all. During the summer before I had left my home town with Harry Whitehead and, with a nigger named Burt, had taken a job as swipe with one of the two horses Harry was campaigning through the fall race meets that year. Mother cried and my sister Mildred, who wanted to get a job as school teacher in our town that fall, stormed and scolded about the house all during the week before I left. They both thought it something disgraceful that one of our family should take a place as a swipe with race horses. I've an idea Mildred thought my taking the place would stand in the way of her getting the job she'd been working so long for.

But after all I had to work and there was no other work to be got. A big lumbering fellow of nineteen couldn't just hang around the house and I had got too big to mow people's lawns and sell newspapers. Little chaps who could get next to people's sympathies by their sizes were always getting jobs away from me. There was one fellow who kept saying to everyone who wanted a lawn mowed or a cistern cleaned that he was saving money to work his way through college, and I used to lay awake nights thinking up ways to injure him without being found out. I kept thinking of wagons running over him and bricks falling on his head as he walked along the street. But never mind him.

I got the place with Harry and I liked Burt fine. We got along splendid together. He was a big nigger with a lazy sprawling body and soft kind eyes, and when it came to a fight he could hit like Jack Johnson. He had Bucephalus, a big black pacing stallion that could do 2.09 or 2.10 if he had to, and I had a little gelding named Doctor Fritz that never lost a race all fall when Harry wanted him to win.

We set out from home late in July in a box car with the two horses, and after that, until late November, we kept moving along to the race meets and the fairs. It was a peachy time for me, I'll say that. Sometimes, now, I think that boys who are raised regular in houses, and never have a fine nigger like Burt for best friend, and go to high schools and college, and never steal anything or get drunk a little, or learn to swear from fellows who know how, or come walking up in front of a grandstand in their shirt sleeves and with dirty horsey pants on when the races are going on and the grandstand is full of people all dressed up—What's the use talking about it? Such fellows don't know nothing at all. They've never had no opportunity.

But I did. Burt taught me how to rub down a horse and put the bandages on after a race and steam a horse out and a lot of valuable things for any man to know. He could wrap a bandage on a horse's leg so smooth that if it had been the same color you would think it was his skin, and I guess he'd have been a big driver, too, and got to the top like Murphy and Walter Cox and the others if he hadn't been black.

Gee whizz, it was fun. You got to a county seat town maybe, say, on a Saturday or Sunday, and the fair began the next Tuesday and lasted until Friday afternoon. Doctor Fritz would be, say, in the 2.25 trot on Tuesday afternoon and on Thursday afternoon Bucephalus would knock 'em cold in the "free-for-all" pace. It left you a lot of time to hang around and listen to horse talk, and see Burt knock some yap cold that got too gay, and you'd find out about horses and men and pick up a lot of stuff you could use all the rest of your life if you had some sense and salted down what you heard and felt and saw.

And then at the end of the week when the race meet was over, and Harry had run home to tend up to his livery stable business, you and Burt hitched the two horses to carts and drove slow and steady across country to the place for the next meeting so as not to overheat the horses, etc., etc., you know.

Gee whizz, gosh amighty, the nice hickorynut and beechnut and oaks and other kinds of trees along the roads, all brown and red, and the good smells, and Burt singing a song that was called Deep River, and the country girls at the windows of houses and everything. You can stick your colleges up your nose for all me. I guess I know where I got my education.

Why, one of those little burgs of towns you come to on the way, say now, on a Saturday afternoon, and Burt says, "let's lay up here." And you did.

And you took the horses to a livery stable and fed them and you got your good clothes out of a box and put them on.

And the town was full of farmers gaping, because they could see you were race horse people, and the kids maybe never see a nigger before and was afraid and run away when the two of us walked down their main street.

And that was before prohibition and all that foolishness, and so you went into a saloon, the two of you, and all the yaps come and stood around, and there was always someone pretended he was horsey and knew things and spoke up and began asking questions, and all you did was to lie and lie all you could about what horses you had, and I said I owned them, and then some fellow said, "Will you have a drink of whisky?" and Burt knocked his eye out the way he could say, offhand like, "Oh, well, all right, I'm agreeable to a little nip. I'll split a quart with you." Gee whizz.

But that isn't what I want to tell my story about. We got home late in November and I promised mother I'd quit the race horses for good. There's a lot of things you've got to promise a mother because she don't know any better.

And so, there not being any work in our town any more than when I left there to go to the races, I went off to Sandusky and got a pretty good place taking care of the horses for a man who owned a teaming and delivery and storage business there. It was a pretty good place with good eats and a day off each week and sleeping on a cot in the big barn, and mostly just shoveling in hay and oats to a lot of big good-enough skates of horses that couldn't have trotted a race with a toad. I wasn't dissatisfied and I could send money home.

And then, as I started to tell you, the fall races come to Sandusky and I got the day off and I went. I left the job at noon and had on my good clothes and my new brown derby hat I'd just bought the Saturday before, and a stand-up collar.

First of all I went downtown and walked about with the dudes. I've always thought to myself, "put up a good front," and so I did it. I had forty dollars in my pocket and so I went into the West House, a big hotel, and walked up to the cigar stand. "Give me three twenty-five cent cigars," I said. There was a lot of horse men and strangers and dressed-up people from other towns standing around in the lobby and in the bar, and I mingled amongst them. In the bar there was a fellow with a cane and a Windsor tie on, that it made me sick to look at him. I like a man to be a man and dress up, but not to go put on that kind of airs. So I pushed him aside, kind of rough, and had me a drink of whisky. And then he looked at me as though he thought he'd get gay, but he changed his mind and didn't say anything. And then I had another drink of whisky, just to show him something, and went out and had a hack out to the races all to myself, and when I got there I bought myself the best seat I could get up in the grandstand, but didn't go in for any of these boxes. That's putting on too many airs.

And so there I was, sitting up in the grandstand as gay as you please and looking down on the swipes coming out with their horses and with their dirty horsey pants on and the horse blankets swung over their shoulders same as I had been doing all the year before. I liked one thing about the same as the other, sitting up there and feeling grand and being down there and looking up at the yaps and feeling grander and more important too. One thing's about as good as another if you take it just right. I've often said that.

Well, right in front of me, in the grandstand that day, there was a fellow with a couple of girls and they was about my age. The young fellow was a nice guy all right. He was the kind maybe that goes to college and then comes to be a lawyer or maybe a newspaper editor or something like that, but he wasn't stuck on himself. There are some of that kind are all right and he was one of the ones.

He had his sister with him and another girl and the sister looked around over his shoulder, accidental at first, not intending to start anything—she wasn't that kind—and her eyes and mine happened to meet.

You know how it is. Gee, she was a peach. She had on a soft dress, kind of a blue stuff, and it looked carelessly made, but was well sewed and made and everything. I knew that much. I blushed when she looked right at me and so did she. She was the nicest girl I've ever seen in my life. She wasn't stuck on herself and she could talk proper grammar without being like a school teacher or something like that. What I mean is, she was O.K. I think maybe her father was well-to-do, but not rich to make her chesty because she was his daughter, as some are. Maybe he owned a drug store or a dry goods store in their home town, or something like that. She never told me and I never asked.

My own people are all O.K. too, when you come to that. My grandfather was Welsh and over in the old country, in Wales, he was—but never mind that.

The first heat of the first race come off and the young fellow setting there with the two girls left them and went down to make a bet. I knew what he was up to, but he didn't talk big and noisy and let everyone around know he was a sport, as some do. He wasn't that kind. Well, he come back and I heard him tell the two girls what horse he'd bet on, and when the heat was trotted they all half got to their feet and acted in the excited, sweaty way people do when they've got money down on a race, and the horse they bet on is up there pretty close at the end, and they think maybe he'll come on with a rush, but he never does because he hasn't got the old juice in him, come right down to it.

And, then, pretty soon, the horses came out for the 2.18 pace and there was a horse in it I knew. He was a horse Bob French had in his string, but Bob didn't own him. He was a horse owned by a Mr. Mathers down at Marietta, Ohio.

This Mr. Mathers had a lot of money and owned a coal mine or something, and he had a swell place out in the country, and he was stuck on race horses, but was a Presbyterian or something, and I think more than likely his wife was one, too, maybe a stiffer one than himself. So he never raced his horses hisself, and the story round the Ohio race tracks was that when one of his horses got ready to go to the races he turned him over to Bob French and pretended to his wife he was sold.

So Bob had the horses and he did pretty much as he pleased and you can't blame Bob; at least, I never did. Sometimes he was out to win and sometimes he wasn't. I never cared much about that when I was swiping a horse. What I did want to know was that my horse had the speed and could go out in front if you wanted him to.

And, as I'm telling you, there was Bob in this race with one of Mr. Mathers' horses, was named "About Ben Ahem" or something like that, and was fast as a streak. He was a gelding and had a mark of 2.21, but could step in .08 or .09.

Because when Burt and I were out, as I've told you, the year before, there was a nigger Burt knew, worked for Mr. Mathers, and we went out there one day when we didn't have no race on at the Marietta Fair and our boss Harry had gone home.

And so everyone was gone to the fair but just this one nigger, and he took us all through Mr. Mathers' swell house and he and Burt tapped a bottle of wine Mr. Mathews had hid in his bedroom, back in a closet, without his wife knowing, and he showed us this Ahem horse. Burt was always stuck on being a driver, but didn't have much chance to get to the top, being a nigger, and he and the other nigger gulped that whole bottle of wine and Burt got a little lit up.

So the nigger let Burt take this About Ben Ahem and step him a mile in a track Mr. Mathers had all to himself, right there on the farm. And Mr. Mathers had one child, a daughter, kinda sick and not very good-looking, and she came home and we had to hustle and get About Ben Ahem stuck back in the barn.

I'm only telling you to get everything straight. At Sandusky, that afternoon I was at the fair, this young fellow with the two girls was fussed, being with the girls and losing his bet. You know how a fellow is that way. One of them was his girl and the other his sister. I had figured that out.

"Gee whizz" I says to myself, "I'm going to give him the dope."

He was mighty nice when I touched him on the shoulder. He and the girls were nice to me right from the start and clear to the end. I'm not blaming them.

And so he leaned back and I gave him the dope on About Ben Ahem. "Don't bet a cent on this first heat because he'll go like an oxen hitched to a plough, but when the first heat is over go right down and lay on your pile." That's what I told him.

Well, I never saw a fellow treat any one sweller. There was a fat man sitting beside the little girl that had looked at me twice by this time, and I at her, and both blushing, and what did he do but have the nerve to turn and ask the fat man to get up and change places with me so I could set with his crowd.

Gee whizz, amighty. There I was. What a chump I was to go and get gay up there in the West House bar, and just because that dude was standing there with a cane and that kind of a necktie on, to go and get all balled up and drink that whisky, just to show off.

Of course, she would know, me setting right beside her and letting her smell of my breath. I could have kicked myself right down out of that grandstand and all around that race track and made a faster record than most of the skates of horses they had there that year.

Because that girl wasn't any mutt of a girl. What wouldn't I have given right then for a stick of chewing gum to chew, or a lozenger, or some licorice, or most anything. I was glad I had those twenty-five cent cigars in my pocket, and right away I give that fellow one and lit one myself. Then that fat man got up and we changed places and there I was plunked down beside her.

They introduced themselves, and the fellow's best girl he had with him, was named Miss Elinor Woodbury, and her father was a manufacturer of barrels from a place called Tiffin, Ohio. And the fellow himself was named Wilbur Wessen and his sister was Miss Lucy Wessen.

I suppose it was their having such swell names got me off my trolley. A fellow, just because he has been a swipe with a race horse, and works taking care of horses for a man in the teaming, delivery and storage business, isn't any better or worse than anyone else. I've often thought that, and said it, too.

But you know how a fellow is. There's something in that kind of nice clothes, and the kind of nice eyes she had, and the way she looked at me, awhile before, over her brother's shoulder, and me looking back at her, and both of us blushing.

I couldn't show her up for a boob, could I?

I made a fool of myself, that's what I did. I said my name was Walter Mathers from Marietta, Ohio, and then I told all three of them the smashingest lie you ever heard. What I said was that my father owned the horse About Ben Ahem, and that he had let him out to this Bob French for racing purposes, because our family was proud and had never gone into racing that way, in our own name, I mean. Then I had got started, and they were all leaning over and listening, and Miss Lucy Wessen's eyes were shining, and I went the whole hog.

I told about our place down at Marietta, and about the big stables and the grand brick house we had on a hill, up above the Ohio River, but I knew enough not to do it in no bragging way. What I did was to start things and then let them drag the rest out of me. I acted just as reluctant to tell as I could. Our family hasn't got any barrel factory, and, since I've known us, we've always been pretty poor, but not asking anything of anyone at that, and my grandfather, over in Wales—but never mind that.

We set there talking like we had known each other for years and years, and I went and told them that my father had been expecting maybe this Bob French wasn't on the square, and had sent me up to Sandusky on the sly to find out what I could.

And I bluffed it through I had found out all about the 2.18 pace in which About Ben Ahem was to start.

I said he would lose the first heat by pacing like a lame cow and then he would come back and skin 'em alive after that. And to back up what I said I took thirty dollars out of my pocket and handed it to Mr. Wilbur Wessen and asked him would he mind, after the first heat, to go down and place it on About Ben Ahem for whatever odds he could get. What I said was that I didn't want Bob French to see me and none of the swipes.

Sure enough the first heat come off and About Ben Ahem went off his stride, up the back stretch, and looked like a wooden horse or a sick one, and come in to be last. Then this Wilbur Wessen went down to the betting place under the grandstand and there I was with the two girls, and when that Miss Woodbury was looking the other way once, Lucy Wessen kinda, with her shoulder you know, kinda touched me. Not just tucking down, I don't mean. You know how a woman can do. They get close, but not getting gay either. You know what they do. Gee whizz.

And then they give me a jolt. What they had done when I didn't know, was to get together, and they had decided Wilbur Wessen would bet fifty dollars, and the two girls had gone and put in ten dollars each of their own money, too. I was sick then, but I was sicker later.

About the gelding, About Ben Ahem, and their winning their money I wasn't worried a lot about that. It come out O.K. Ahem stepped the next three heats like a bushel of spoiled eggs going to market before they could be found out, and Wilbur Wessen had got nine to two for the money. There was something else eating at me.

Because Wilbur come back after he had bet the money, and after that he spent most of his time talking to that Miss Woodbury, and Lucy Wessen and I was left alone together like on a desert island. Gee, if I'd only been on the square or if there had been any way of getting myself on the square. There ain't any Walter Mathers, like I said to her and them, and there hasn't ever been one, but if there was, I bet I'd go to Marietta, Ohio, and shoot him tomorrow.

There I was, big boob that I am. Pretty soon the race was over, and Wilbur had gone down and collected our money, and we had a hack down town, and he stood us a swell dinner at the West House, and a bottle of champagne beside.

And I was with that girl and she wasn't saying much, and I wasn't saying much either. One thing I know. She wasn't stuck on me because of the lie about my father being rich and all that. There's a way you know. . . . Craps amighty. There's a kind of girl you see just once in your life, and if you don't get busy and make hay then you're gone for good and all and might as well go jump off a bridge. They give you a look from inside of them somewhere, and it ain't no vamping, and what it means is—you want that girl to be your wife, and you want nice things around her like flowers and swell clothes, and you want her to have the kids you're going to have, and you want good music played and no ragtime. Gee whizz.

There's a place over near Sandusky, across a kind of bay, and it's called Cedar Point. And when we had had that dinner we went over to it in a launch, all by ourselves. Wilbur and Miss Lucy and that Miss Woodbury had to catch a ten o'clock train back to Tiffin, Ohio, because when you're out with girls like that you can't get careless and miss any trains and stay out all night like you can with some kinds of Janes.

And Wilbur blowed himself to the launch and it cost him fifteen cold plunks, but I wouldn't ever have knew it if I hadn't listened. He wasn't no tin horn kind of a sport.

Over at the Cedar Point place we didn't stay around where there was a gang of common kind of cattle at all.

There was big dance halls and dining places for yaps, and there was a beach you could walk along and get where it was dark, and we went there.

She didn't talk hardly at all and neither did I, and I was thinking how glad I was my mother was all right, and always made us kids learn to eat with a fork at table and not swill soup and not be noisy and rough like a gang you see around a race track that way.

Then Wilbur and his girl went away up the beach and Lucy and I set down in a dark place where there was some roots of old trees the water had washed up, and after that, the time, till we had to go back in the launch and they had to catch their trains, wasn't nothing at all. It went like winking your eye.

Here's how it was. The place we were setting in was dark, like I said, and there was the roots from that old stump sticking up like arms, and there was a watery smell, and the night was like—as if you could put your hand out and feel it—so warm and soft and dark and sweet like an orange.

I most cried and I most swore and I most jumped up and danced, I was so mad and happy and sad.

When Wilbur come back from being alone with his girl, and she saw him coming, Lucy she says, "We got to go to the train now," and she was most crying, too, but she never knew nothing I knew, and she couldn't be so all busted up. And then, before Wilbur and Miss Woodbury got up to where we was, she put her face up and kissed me quick and put her head up against me and she was all quivering and—Gee whizz.

Sometimes I hope I have cancer and die. I guess you know what I mean. We went in the launch across the bay to the train like that, and it was dark too. She whispered and said it was like she and I could get out of the boat and walk on the water, and it sounded foolish, but I knew what she meant.

And then quick, we were right at the depot, and there was a big gang of yaps, the kind that goes to the fairs, and crowded and milling around like cattle, and how could I tell her? "It won't be long because you'll write and I'll write to you." That's all she said.

I got a chance like a hay barn afire. A swell chance I got.

And maybe she would write me, down at Marietta that way, and the letter would come back, and stamped on the front of it by the U.S.A. "there ain't any such guy," or something like that, whatever they stamp on a letter that way.

And me trying to pass myself off for a bigbug and a swell—to her, as decent a little body as God ever made. Craps amighty. A swell chance I got.

And then the train come and she got on, and Wilbur Wessen come and shook hands with me, and that Miss Woodbury was nice too, and bowed to me and I at her and the train went and I busted out and cried like a kid.

Gee, I could have run after that train and made Dan Patch look like a freight train after a wreck, but socks amighty, what was the use? Did you ever see such a fool?

I'll bet you what—if I had an arm broke right now or a train had run over my foot—I wouldn't go to no doctor at all. I'd go set down and let her hurt and hurt—that's what I 'd do.

I'll bet you what—if I hadn't a drunk that booze I'd a never been such a boob as to go tell such a lie—that couldn't never be made straight to a lady like her.

I wish I had that fellow right here that had on a Windsor tie and carried a cane. I'd smash him for fair. Gosh darn his eyes. He's a big fool—that's what he is.

And if I'm not another you just go find me one and I'll quit working and be a bum and give him my job. I don't care nothing for working and earning money and saving it for no such boob as myself.

WILLA CATHER

# ❧ *Paul's Case*

It was Paul's afternoon to appear before the faculty of the Pittsburgh High School to account for his various misdemeanors. He had been suspended a week ago, and his father had called at the Principal's office and confessed his perplexity about his son. Paul entered the faculty room suave and smiling. His clothes were a trifle outgrown, and the tan velvet on the collar of his open overcoat was frayed and worn; but for all that there was something of the dandy about him, and he wore an opal pin in his neatly knotted black four-in-hand, and a red carnation in his buttonhole. This latter adornment the faculty somehow felt was not properly significant of the contrite spirit befitting a boy under the ban of suspension.

Paul was tall for his age and very thin, with high, cramped shoulders and a narrow chest. His eyes were remarkable for a certain hysterical brilliancy, and he continually used them in a conscious, theatrical sort of way, peculiarly offensive in a boy. The pupils were abnormally large, as though he were addicted to belladonna, but there was a glassy glitter about them which that drug does not produce.

When questioned by the Principal as to why he was there, Paul stated, politely enough, that he wanted to come back to school. This was a lie, but Paul was quite accustomed to lying; found it, indeed, indispensable for overcoming friction. His teachers were asked to state their respective charges against him, which they did with such a rancor and aggrievedness as evinced that this was not a usual case. Disorder and impertinence were among the offenses named, yet each of his instructors felt that it was scarcely possible to put into words the real cause of the trouble, which lay in a sort of hysterically defiant manner of the boy's; in the contempt which they all knew he felt for them, and which he seemingly made not the least effort to conceal. Once, when he had been making a synopsis of a paragraph at the blackboard, his English teacher had stepped to his side and attempted to guide his hand. Paul had started back with a shudder and thrust his hands violently behind him. The astonished woman could scarcely have been more hurt and embarrassed had he struck at her. The insult was so involuntary and definitely personal as to be unforgettable. In one way and another, he had made all his teachers, men and women alike, conscious of the same feeling of physical aversion. In one class he habitually sat with his hand shading his eyes; in another he always looked out of the window during the recitation; in another he made a running commentary on the lecture, with humorous intent.

His teachers felt this afternoon that his whole attitude was symbolized by his shrug and his flippantly red carnation flower, and they fell upon him without mercy, his English teacher leading the pack. He stood through it smiling, his pale lips parted over his white teeth. (His lips were continually twitching, and he had a habit of raising his eyebrows that was contemptuous and irritating to the last degree.) Older boys than Paul had broken down and shed tears under that ordeal, but his set smile did not once desert him, and his only sign of discomfort was the nervous trembling of the fingers that toyed with the buttons of his overcoat, and an occasional jerking of the other hand which held his hat. Paul was always smiling, always glancing about him, seeming to feel that people might be watching him and trying to detect something. This conscious expression, since it was as far as possible from boyish mirthfulness, was usually attributed to insolence or "smartness."

As the inquisition proceeded, one of his instructors repeated an impertinent remark of the boy's, and the Principal asked him whether he thought that a courteous speech to make to a woman. Paul shrugged his shoulders slightly and his eyebrows twitched.

"I don't know," he replied. "I didn't mean to be polite or impolite, either. I guess it's a sort of way I have, of saying things regardless."

The Principal asked him whether he didn't think that a way it would be well to get rid of. Paul grinned and said he guessed so. When he was told that he could go, he bowed gracefully and went out. His bow was like a repetition of the scandalous red carnation.

His teachers were in despair, and his drawing master voiced the feeling of them all when he declared there was something about the boy which none of them understood. He added: "I don't really believe that smile of his comes altogether from insolence; there's something sort of haunted about it. The boy is not strong, for one thing. There is something wrong about the fellow."

The drawing master had come to realize that, in looking at Paul, one saw only his white teeth and the forced animation of his eyes. One warm afternoon the boy had gone to sleep at his drawing board, and his master had noted with amazement what a white, blue-veined face it was; drawn and wrinkled like an old man's about the eyes, the lips twitching even in his sleep.

His teachers left the building dissatisfied and unhappy; humiliated to have felt so vindictive toward a mere boy, to have uttered this feeling in cutting terms, and to have set each other on, as it were, in the gruesome game of intemperate reproach. One of them remembered having seen a miserable street cat set at bay by a ring of tormentors.

As for Paul, he ran down the hill whistling the Soldiers' Chorus from *Faust*, looking wildly behind him now and then to see whether some of his teachers were not there to witness his light-heartedness. As it was now late in the afternoon and Paul was on duty that evening as usher at Carnegie Hall, he decided that he would not go home to supper.

When he reached the concert hall the doors were not yet open. It was chilly outside, and he decided to go up into the picture gallery—always deserted at this hour—where there were some of Raffaelli's [1850–1924; French impressionist painter] gay studies of Paris streets and an airy blue Venetian scene or two that always exhilarated him. He was delighted to find no one in the gallery but the old guard, who sat in the corner, a newspaper on his knee, a black patch over one eye and the other closed. Paul possessed himself of the place and walked confidently up and down, whistling under his breath. After a while he sat down before a blue Rico [1833–1908; Spanish landscape artist] and lost himself. When he bethought him to look at his watch, it was after seven o'clock, and he rose with a start and ran downstairs, making a face at Augustus Caesar, peering out from the cast-room, and an evil gesture at the Venus of Milo as he passed her on the stairway.

When Paul reached the ushers' dressing-room half a dozen boys were there already, and he began excitedly to tumble into his uniform. It was one of the few that at all approached fitting, and Paul thought it very becoming—though he knew the tight, straight coat accentuated his narrow chest, about which he was exceedingly sensitive. He was always excited while he dressed, twanging all over to the tuning of the strings and the preliminary flourishes of the horns in the music-room; but tonight he seemed quite beside himself, and he teased and plagued the boys until, telling him that he was crazy, they put him down on the floor and sat on him.

Somewhat calmed by his suppression, Paul dashed out to the front of the house to seat the early comers. He was a model usher. Gracious and smiling he ran up and down the aisles. Nothing was too much trouble for him; he carried messages and brought programs as though it were his greatest pleasure in life, and all the people in his section thought him a charming boy, feeling that he remembered and admired them. As the house filled, he grew more and more vivacious and animated, and the color came to his cheeks and lips. It was very much as though this were a great reception and Paul were the host. Just as the musicians came out to take their places, his English teacher arrived with checks for the seats which a prominent manufacturer had taken for the season. She betrayed some embarrassment when she handed Paul the tickets, and a *hauteur* which subsequently made her feel very foolish. Paul was startled for a moment, and had the feeling of wanting to put her out; what business had she here among all these fine people and gay colors? He looked her over and decided that she was not appropriately dressed and must be a fool to sit downstairs in such togs. The tickets had probably been sent her out of kindness, he reflected, as he put down a seat for her, and she had about as much right to sit there as he had.

When the symphony began Paul sank into one of the rear seats with a long sigh of relief, and lost himself as he had done before the Rico. It was not that symphonies, as such, meant anything in particular to Paul, but the first sigh of the instruments seemed to free some hilarious spirit within him; something that struggled there like the Genius in the bottle found by the Arab fisherman. He felt a sudden zest of life; the lights danced before his eyes and the concert hall blazed into unimaginable splendor. When the soprano soloist came on, Paul forgot even the nastiness of his teacher's being there, and gave himself up to the peculiar intoxication such personages always had for him. The soloist chanced to be a German woman, by no means in her first youth, and the mother of many children; but she wore a satin gown and a tiara, and she had that indefinable air of achievement, that world-shine upon her, which always blinded Paul to any possible defects.

After a concert was over, Paul was often irritable and wretched until he got to sleep,—and tonight he was even more than usually restless. He had the feeling of not being able to let down; of its being impossible to give up this delicious excitement which was the only thing that could be called living at all. During the last number he withdrew and, after hastily changing his clothes in the dressing-room, slipped out to the side door where the singer's carriage stood. Here he began pacing rapidly up and down the walk, waiting to see her come out.

Over yonder the Schenley, in its vacant stretch, loomed big and square through the fine rain, the windows of its twelve stories glowing like those of a lighted cardboard house under a Christmas tree. All the actors and singers of any importance stayed there when they were in the city, and a number of the big manufacturers of the place lived there in the winter. Paul had often hung about the hotel, watching the people go in and out, longing to enter and leave schoolmasters and dull care behind him forever.

At last the singer came out, accompanied by the conductor, who helped her into her carriage and closed the door with a cordial *auf wiedersehen*,—which set Paul to wondering whether she were not an old sweetheart of his. Paul followed the carriage over to the hotel, walking so rapidly as not to be far from the entrance when the singer alighted and disappeared behind the swinging glass doors which were opened by a Negro in a tall hat and a long coat. In the moment that the door was ajar, it seemed to Paul that he, too, entered. He seemed to feel himself go after her up the steps, into the warm, lighted building, into an exotic, a tropical world of shiny, glistening surfaces and basking ease. He reflected upon the mysterious dishes that were brought into the dining-room, the green bottles in buckets of ice, as he had seen them in the supper party pictures of the Sunday supplement. A quick gust of wind brought the rain down with sudden vehemence, and Paul was startled to find that he was still outside in the slush of the gravel driveway; that his boots were letting in the water and his scanty overcoat was clinging wet about him; that the lights in front of the concert hall were out, and that the rain was driving in sheets between him and the orange glow of the windows above him. There it was, what he wanted—tangibly before him, like the fairy world of a Christmas pantomime; as the rain beat in his face, Paul wondered whether he were destined always to shiver in the black night outside, looking up at it.

He turned and walked reluctantly toward the car tracks. The end had to come some time; his father in his night-clothes at the top of the stairs, explanations that did not explain, hastily improvised fictions that were forever tripping him up, his upstairs room and its horrible yellow wall paper, the creaking bureau with the greasy plush collar-box, and over his painted wooden bed the pictures of George Washington and John Calvin, and the framed motto, "Feed my Lambs," which had been worked in red worsted by his mother, whom Paul could not remember.

Half an hour later, Paul alighted from the Negley Avenue car and went slowly down one of the side streets off the main thoroughfare. It was a highly respectable street, where all the houses were exactly alike, and where business men of moderate means begot and reared large families of children, all of whom went to Sabbath-school and learned the shorter catechism, and were interested in arithmetic; all of whom were as exactly alike as their homes, and of a piece with the monotony in which they lived. Paul never went up Cordelia Street without a shudder of loathing. His home was next the house of the Cumberland minister. He approached it tonight with the nerveless sense of defeat, the hopeless feeling of sinking back forever into ugliness and commonness that he had always had when he came home. The moment he turned into Cordelia Street he felt the waters close above his head. After each of these orgies of living, he experienced all the physical depression which follows a debauch; the loathing of respectable beds, of common food, of a house permeated by kitchen odors; a shuddering repulsion for the flavorless, colorless mass of everyday existence; a morbid desire for cool things and soft lights and fresh flowers.

The nearer he approached the house, the more absolutely unequal Paul felt to the sight of it all; his ugly sleeping chamber; the cold bathroom with the grimy zinc tub, the cracked mirror, the dripping spiggots; his father, at the top of the stairs, his hairy legs sticking out from his nightshirt, his feet thrust into carpet slippers. He was so much later than usual that there would certainly be inquiries and reproaches. Paul stopped short before the door. He felt that he could not be accosted by his father tonight; that he could not toss again on that miserable bed. He would not go in. He would tell his father that he had no car fare, and it was raining so hard he had gone home with one of the boys and stayed all night.

Meanwhile, he was wet and cold. He went around to the back of the house and tried one of the basement windows, found it open, raised it cautiously, and scrambled down the cellar wall to the floor. There he stood, holding his breath, terrified by the noise he had made; but the floor above him was silent, and there was no creak on the stairs. He found a soap-box, and carried it over to the soft ring of light that streamed from the furnace door, and sat down. He was horribly afraid of rats, so he did not try to sleep, but sat looking distrustfully at the dark, still terrified lest he might have awakened his father. In such reactions, after one of the experiences which made days and nights out of the dreary blanks of the calendar, when his senses were deadened, Paul's head was always singularly clear. Suppose his father had heard him getting in at the window and had come down and shot him for a burglar? Then, again, suppose his father had come down, pistol in hand, and he had cried out in time to save himself, and his father had been horrified to think how nearly he had killed him? Then, again, suppose a day should come when his father would remember that night, and wish there had been no warning cry to stay his hand? With this last supposition Paul entertained himself until daybreak.

The following Sunday was fine; the sodden November chill was broken by the last flash of autumnal summer. In the morning Paul had to go to church and Sabbath-school, as always. On seasonable Sunday afternoons the burghers of Cordelia Street usually sat out on their front "stoops," and talked to their neighbors on the next stoop, or called to those across the street in neighborly fashion. The men sat placidly on gay cushions placed upon the steps that led down to the sidewalk, while the women, in their Sunday "waists," sat in rockers on the cramped porches, pretending to be greatly at their ease. The children played in the streets; there were so many of them that the place resembled the recreation grounds of a kindergarten. The men on the steps—all in their shirt sleeves, their vests unbuttoned—sat with their legs well apart, their stomachs comfortably protruding, and talked of the prices of things, or told anecdotes of the sagacity of their various chiefs and overlords. They occasionally looked over the multitude of squabbling children, listened affectionately to their high-pitched, nasal voices, smiling to see their own proclivities reproduced in their offspring, and interspersed their legends of the iron kings with remarks about their sons' progress at school, their grades in arithmetic, and the amounts they had saved in their toy banks. On this last Sunday of November, Paul sat all the afternoon on the lowest step of his stoop, staring into the street, while his sisters, in their rockers, were talking to the minister's daughters next door about how many shirtwaists they had made in the last week, and how many waffles someone had eaten at the last church supper. When the weather was

warm, and his father was in a particularly jovial frame of mind, the girls made
lemonade, which was always brought out in a red-glass pitcher, ornamented
with forget-me-nots in blue enamel. This the girls thought very fine, and the
neighbors joked about the suspicious color of the pitcher.

Today Paul's father, on the top step, was talking to a young man who
shifted a restless baby from knee to knee. He happened to be the young man
who was daily held up to Paul as a model, and after whom it was his father's
dearest hope that he would pattern. This young man was of a ruddy com-
plexion, with a compressed, red mouth, and faded, nearsighted eyes, over which
he wore thick spectacles, with gold bows that curved about his ears. He was
clerk to one of the magnates of a great steel corporation, and was looked upon
in Cordelia Street as a young man with a future. There was a story that, some
five years ago—he was now barely twenty-six—he had been a trifle "dissipated,"
but in order to curb his appetites and save the loss of time and strength that a
sowing of wild oats might have entailed, he had taken his chief's advice, oft
reiterated to his employees, and at twenty-one had married the first woman
whom he could persuade to share his fortunes. She happened to be an angular
school mistress, much older than he, who also wore thick glasses, and who had
now borne him four children, all near-sighted, like herself.

The young man was relating how his chief, now cruising in the Mediterranean, kept in touch with all the details of the business, arranging his office
hours on his yacht just as though he were at home, and "knocking off work
enough to keep two stenographers busy." His father told, in turn, the plan his
corporation was considering, of putting in an electric railway plant at Cairo.
Paul snapped his teeth; he had an awful apprehension that they might spoil it
all before he got there. Yet he rather liked to hear these legends of the iron
kings, that were told and retold on Sundays and holidays; these stories of
palaces in Venice, yachts on the Mediterranean, and high play at Monte Carlo
appealed to his fancy, and he was interested in the triumphs of cash boys[2] who
had become famous, though he had no mind for the cash-boy stage.

After supper was over, and he had helped to dry the dishes, Paul nervously
asked his father whether he could go to George's to get some help in his
geometry, and still more nervously asked for car fare. This latter request he had
to repeat, as his father, on principle, did not like to hear requests for money,
whether much or little. He asked Paul whether he could not go to some boy
who lived nearer, and told him that he ought not to leave his school work until
Sunday; but he gave him the dime. He was not a poor man, but he had a
worthy ambition to come up in the world. His only reason for allowing Paul to
usher was that he thought a boy ought to be earning a little.

Paul bounded upstairs, scrubbed the greasy odor of the dishwater from his
hands with the ill-smelling soap he hated, and then shook over his fingers a few

---

[2] Messengers who carry money or chips from the gambling table to the cashier and
back. [Ed.]

drops of violet water from the bottle he kept hidden in his drawer. He left the house with his geometry conspicuously under his arm, and the moment he got out of Cordelia Street and boarded a downtown car, he shook off the lethargy of two deadening days, and began to live again.

The leading juvenile of the permanent stock company which played at one of the downtown theaters was an acquaintance of Paul's, and the boy had been invited to drop in at the Sunday night rehearsals whenever he could. For more than a year Paul had spent every available moment loitering about Charley Edwards's dressing-room. He had won a place among Edwards's following not only because the young actor, who could not afford to employ a dresser, often found him useful, but because he recognized in Paul something akin to what churchmen term "vocation."

It was at the theater and at Carnegie Hall that Paul really lived; the rest was but a sleep and a forgetting. This was Paul's fairy tale, and it had for him all the allurement of a secret love. The moment he inhaled the gassy, painty, dusty odor behind the scenes, he breathed like a prisoner set free, and felt within him the possibility of doing or saying splendid, brilliant things. The moment the cracked orchestra beat out the overture from *Martha*, or jerked at the serenade from *Rigoletto*, all stupid and ugly things slid from him, and his senses were deliciously, yet delicately fired.

Perhaps it was because, in Paul's world, the natural nearly always wore the guise of ugliness, that a certain element of artificiality seemed to him necessary in beauty. Perhaps it was because his experience of life elsewhere was so full of Sabbath-school picnics, petty economies, wholesome advice as to how to succeed in life, and the unescapable odors of cooking that he found this existence so alluring, these smartly-clad men and women so attractive, that he was so moved by these starry apple orchards that bloomed perennially under the limelight.

It would be difficult to put it strongly enough how convincingly the stage entrance of that theater was for Paul the actual portal of Romance. Certainly none of the company ever suspected it, least of all Charley Edwards. It was very like the old stories that used to float about London of fabulously rich Jews, who had subterranean halls, with palms, and fountains, and soft lamps and richly apparelled women who never saw the disenchanting light of London day. So, in the midst of that smoke-palled city, enamored of figures and grimy toil, Paul had his secret temple, his wishing-carpet, his bit of blue-and-white Mediterranean shore bathed in perpetual sunshine.

Several of Paul's teachers had a theory that his imagination had been perverted by garish fiction; but the truth was, he scarcely ever read at all. The books at home were not such as would either tempt or corrupt a youthful mind, and as for reading the novels that some of his friends urged upon him—well, he got what he wanted much more quickly from music; any sort of music, from an orchestra to a barrel organ. He needed only the spark, the indescribable thrill that made his imagination master of his senses, and he could make plots and pictures enough of his own. It was equally true that he was not stage-struck—not, at any rate, in the usual acceptation of that expression. He had no desire to become an actor, any more than he had to become a musician. He felt no necessity to do any of these things; what he wanted was to see, to be in the atmosphere, float on the wave of it, to be carried out, blue league after blue league, away from everything.

After a night behind the scenes, Paul found the schoolroom more than ever repulsive; the bare floors and naked walls; the prosy men who never wore frock coats, or violets in their buttonholes; the women with their dull gowns, shrill voices, and pitiful seriousness about prepositions that govern the dative. He could not bear to have the other pupils think, for a moment, that he took these people seriously; he must convey to them that he considered it all trivial, and was there only by way of a joke, anyway. He had autograph pictures of all the members of the stock company which he showed his classmates, telling them the most incredible stories of his familiarity with these people, of his acquaintance with the soloists who came to Carnegie Hall, his suppers with them and the flowers he sent them. When these stories lost their effect, and his audience grew listless, he would bid all the boys good-by, announcing that he was going to travel for a while; going to Naples, to California, to Egypt. Then, next Monday, he would slip back, conscious and nervously smiling; his sister was ill, and he would have to defer his voyage until spring.

Matters went steadily worse with Paul at school. In the itch to let his instructors know how heartily he despised them, and how thoroughly he was appreciated elsewhere, he mentioned once or twice that he had no time to fool with theorems; adding—with a twitch of the eyebrows and a touch of that nervous bravado which so perplexed them—that he was helping the people down at the stock company; they were old friends of his.

The upshot of the matter was, that the Principal went to Paul's father, and Paul was taken out of school and put to work. The manager at Carnegie Hall was told to get another usher in his stead; the doorkeeper at the theater was warned not to admit him to the house; and Charley Edwards remorsefully promised the boy's father not to see him again.

The members of the stock company were vastly amused when some of Paul's stories reached them—especially the women. They were hard-working women, most of them supporting indolent husbands or brothers, and they laughed rather bitterly at having stirred the boy to such fervid and florid inventions. They agreed with the faculty and with his father, that Paul's was a bad case.

The east-bound train was plowing through a January snowstorm; the dull dawn was beginning to show gray when the engine whistled a mile out of Newark. Paul started up from the seat where he had lain curled in uneasy slumber, rubbed the breath-misted window glass with his hand, and peered out. The snow was whirling in curling eddies above the white bottom lands, and the drifts lay already deep in the fields and along the fences, while here and there the long dead grass and dried weed stalks protruded black above it. Lights shone from the scattered houses, and a gang of laborers who stood beside the track waved their lanterns.

Paul had slept very little, and he felt grimy and uncomfortable. He had made the all-night journey in a day coach because he was afraid if he took a Pullman he might be seen by some Pittsburgh business man who had noticed him in Denny & Carson's office. When the whistle woke him, he clutched quickly at his breast pocket, glancing about him with an uncertain smile. But the little, clay-bespattered Italians were still sleeping, the slatternly women across the aisle were in open-mouthed oblivion, and even the crumby, crying babies were for the nonce stilled. Paul settled back to struggle with his impatience as best he could.

When he arrived at the Jersey City station, he hurried through his breakfast, manifestly ill at ease and keeping a sharp eye about him. After he reached the Twenty-third Street station, he consulted a cabman, and had himself driven to a men's furnishing establishment which was just opening for the day. He spent upward to two hours there, buying with endless reconsidering and great care. His new street suit he put on in the fitting-room; the frock coat and dress clothes he had bundled into the cab with his new shirts. Then he drove to a hatter's and a shoe house. His next errand was at Tiffany's, where he selected silver-mounted brushes and a scarf-pin. He would not wait to have his silver marked, he said. Lastly, he stopped at a trunk shop on Broadway, and had his purchases packed into various traveling bags.

It was a little after one o'clock when he drove up to the Waldorf, and, after settling with the cabman, went into the office. He registered from Washington; said his mother and father had been abroad, and that he had come down to await the arrival of their steamer. He told his story plausibly and had no trouble, since he offered to pay for them in advance, in engaging his rooms; a sleeping-room, sitting room and bath.

Not once, but a hundred times Paul had planned this entry into New York. He had gone over every detail of it with Charley Edwards, and in his scrap book at home there were pages of description about New York hotels, cut from the Sunday papers.

When he was shown to his sitting room on the eighth floor, he saw at a glance that everything was as it should be; there was but one detail in his mental picture that the place did not realize, so he rang for the bell boy and sent him down for flowers. He moved about nervously until the boy returned, putting away his new linen and fingering it delightedly as he did so. When the flowers came, he put them hastily into water, and then tumbled into a hot bath. Presently he came out of his white bathroom, resplendent in his new silk underwear, and playing with the tassels of his red robe. The snow was whirling so fiercely outside his windows that he could scarcely see across the street; but within, the air was deliciously soft and fragrant. He put the violets and jonquils on the tabouret beside the couch, and threw himself down with a long sigh, covering himself with a Roman blanket. He was thoroughly tired; he had been in such haste, he had stood up to such a strain, covered so much ground in the last twenty-four hours, that he wanted to think how it had all come about. Lulled by the sound of the wind, the warm air, and the cool fragrance of the flowers, he sank into deep, drowsy retrospection.

It had been wonderfully simple; when they had shut him out of the theater and concert hall, when they had taken away his bone, the whole thing was virtually determined. The rest was a mere matter of opportunity. The only thing that at all surprised him was his own courage—for he realized well enough that he had always been tormented by fear, a sort of apprehensive dread that, of late years, as the meshes of the lies he had told closed about him, had been pulling the muscles of his body tighter and tighter. Until now, he could not remember a time when he had not been dreading something. Even when he was a little boy, it was always there—behind him, or before, or on either side. There had always been the shadowed corner, the dark place into which he dared not look but from which something seemed always to be watching him—and Paul had done things that were not pretty to watch, he knew.

But now he had a curious sense of relief, as though he had at last thrown down the gauntlet to the thing in the corner.

Yet it was but a day since he had been sulking in the traces; but yesterday afternoon that he had been sent to the bank with Denny & Carson's deposit, as usual—but this time he was instructed to leave the book to be balanced. There was above two thousand dollars in checks, and nearly a thousand in the bank notes which he had taken from the book and quietly transferred to his pocket. At the bank he had made out a new deposit slip. His nerves had been steady enough to permit of his returning to the office, where he had finished his work and asked for a full day's holiday tomorrow, Saturday, giving a perfectly reasonable pretext. The bank book, he knew, would not be returned before Monday or Tuesday, and his father would be out of town for the next week. From the time he slipped the bank notes into his pocket until he boarded the night train for New York, he had not known a moment's hesitation.

How astonishingly easy it had all been; here he was, the thing done; and this time there would be no awakening, no figure at the top of the stairs. He watched the snowflakes whirling by his window until he fell asleep.

When he awoke, it was four o'clock in the afternoon. He bounded up with a start; one of his precious days gone already! He spent nearly an hour in dressing, watching every stage of his toilet carefully in the mirror. Everything was quite perfect; he was exactly the kind of boy he had always wanted to be.

When he went downstairs, Paul took a carriage and drove up Fifth Avenue toward the Park. The snow had somewhat abated; carriages and tradesmen's wagons were hurrying soundlessly to and fro in the winter twilight; boys in woolen mufflers were shoveling off the doorsteps; the avenue stages made fine spots of color against the white street. Here and there on the corners whole flower gardens blooming behind glass windows, against which the snowflakes stuck and melted; violets, roses, carnations, lilies of the valley—somehow vastly more lovely and alluring that they blossomed thus unnaturally in the snow. The Park itself was a wonderful stage winter-piece.

When he returned, the pause of the twilight had ceased, and the tune of the streets had changed. The snow was falling faster, lights streamed from the hotels that reared their many stories fearlessly up into the storm, defying the raging Atlantic winds. A long, black stream of carriages poured down the avenue, intersected here and there by other streams, tending horizontally. There were a score of cabs about the entrance of his hotel, and his driver had to wait. Boys in livery were running in and out of the awning stretched across the sidewalk, up and down the red velvet carpet laid from the door to the street. Above, about, within it all, was the rumble and roar, the hurry and toss of thousands of human beings as hot for pleasure as himself, and on every side of him towered the glaring affirmation of the omnipotence of wealth.

The boy set his teeth and drew his shoulders together in a spasm of realization; the plot of all dramas, the text of all romances, the nerve-stuff of all sensations was whirling about him like the snowflakes. He burnt like a faggot in a tempest.

When Paul came down to dinner, the music of the orchestra floated up the elevator shaft to greet him. As he stepped into the thronged corridor, he sank back into one of the chairs against the wall to get his breath. The lights, the chatter, the perfumes, the bewildering medley of color—he had, for a moment, the feeling of not being able to stand it. But only for a moment; these were his own people, he told himself. He went slowly about the corridors, through the writing-rooms, smoking-rooms, reception-rooms, as though he were exploring the chambers of an enchanted palace, built and peopled for him alone.

When he reached the dining room he sat down at a table near a window. The flowers, the white linen, the many-colored wine glasses, the gay toilettes of the women, the low popping of corks, the undulating repetitions of the *Blue Danube* from the orchestra, all flooded Paul's dream with bewildering radiance. When the roseate tinge of his champagne was added—that cold, precious, bubbling stuff that creamed and foamed in his glass—Paul wondered that there were honest men in the world at all. This was what all the world was fighting for, he reflected; this was what all the struggle was about. He doubted the reality of his past. Had he ever known a place called Cordelia Street, a place where fagged-looking business men boarded the early car? Mere rivets in a machine they seemed to Paul,—sickening men, with combings of children's hair always hanging to their coats, and the smell of cooking in their clothes. Cordelia Street—Ah, that belonged to another time and country! Had he not always been thus, had he not sat here night after night, from as far back as he could remember, looking pensively over just such shimmering textures, and slowly twirling the stem of a glass like this one between his thumb and middle finger? He rather thought he had.

He was not in the least abashed or lonely. He had no especial desire to meet or to know any of these people; all he demanded was the right to look on and conjecture, to watch the pageant. The mere stage properties were all he contended for. Nor was he lonely later in the evening, in his loge at the Opera. He was entirely rid of his nervous misgivings, of his forced aggressiveness, of the imperative desire to show himself different from his surroundings. He felt now that his surroundings explained him. Nobody questioned the purple; he had only to wear it passively. He had only to glance down at his dress coat to reassure himself that here it would be impossible for anyone to humiliate him.

He found it hard to leave his beautiful sitting room to go to bed that night, and sat long watching the raging storm from his turret window. When he went to sleep, it was with the lights turned on in his bedroom; partly because of his old timidity, and partly so that, if he should wake in the night, there would be no wretched moment of doubt, no horrible suspicion of yellow wall paper, or of Washington and Calvin above his bed.

On Sunday morning the city was practically snow-bound. Paul breakfasted late, and in the afternoon he fell in with a wild San Francisco boy, a freshman at Yale, who said he had run down for a "little flyer" [reckless adventure] over Sunday. The young man offered to show Paul the night side of the town, and the two boys went off together after dinner, not returning to the hotel until seven o'clock the next morning. They had started out in the confiding warmth of a champagne friendship, but their parting in the elevator was singularly cool. The freshman pulled himself together to make his train, and Paul went to bed. He awoke at two o'clock in the afternoon, very thirsty and dizzy, and rang for ice water, coffee, and the Pittsburgh papers.

On the part of the hotel management, Paul excited no suspicion. There was this to be said for him, that he wore his spoils with dignity and in no way made himself conspicuous. His chief greediness lay in his ears and eyes, and his excesses were not offensive ones. His dearest pleasures were the gray winter twilights in his sitting room; his quiet enjoyment of his flowers, his clothes, his wide divan, his cigarette and his sense of power. He could not remember a time when he had felt so at peace with himself. The mere release from the necessity of petty lying, lying every day and every day, restored his self-respect. He had never lied for pleasure, even at school; but to make himself noticed and admired, to assert his difference from other Cordelia Street boys; and he felt a good deal more manly, more honest, even, now that he had no need for boastful pretensions, now that he could, as his actor friends used to say, "dress the part." It was characteristic that remorse did not occur to him. His golden days went by without a shadow, and he made each as perfect as he could.

On the eighth day after his arrival in New York, he found the whole affair exploited in the Pittsburgh papers, exploited with a wealth of detail which indicated that local news of a sensational nature was at a low ebb. The firm of Denny & Carson announced that the boy's father had refunded the full amount of his theft, and that they had no intention of prosecuting. The Cumberland minister had been interviewed, and expressed his hope of yet reclaiming the motherless lad, and Paul's Sabbath-school teacher declared that she would spare no effort to that end. The rumor had reached Pittsburgh that the boy had been seen in a New York hotel, and his father had gone East to find him and bring him home.

Paul had just come in to dress for dinner; he sank into a chair, weak in the knees, and clasped his head in his hands. It was to be worse than jail, even; the tepid waters of Cordelia Street were to close over him finally and forever. The gray monotony stretched before him in hopeless, unrelieved years; Sabbath-school, Young People's Meeting, the yellow-papered room, the damp dish-towels; it all rushed back upon him with sickening vividness. He had the old feeling that the orchestra had suddenly stopped, the sinking sensation that the play was over. The sweat broke out on his face, and he sprang to his feet, looked about him with his white, conscious smile, and winked at himself in the mirror. With something of the childish belief in miracles with which he had so often gone to class, all his lessons unlearned, Paul dressed and dashed whistling down the corridor to the elevator.

He had no sooner entered the dining room and caught the measure of the music, than his remembrance was lightened by his old elastic power of claiming the moment, mounting with it, and finding it all sufficient. The glare and glitter about him, the mere scenic accessories had again, and for the last time, their old potency. He would show himself that he was game, he would finish the thing splendidly. He doubted, more than ever, the existence of Cordelia Street, and for the first time he drank his wine recklessly. Was he not, after all, one of these fortunate beings? Was he not still himself, and in his own place? He drummed a nervous accompaniment to the music and looked about him, telling himself over and over that it had paid.

He reflected drowsily, to the swell of the violin and the chill sweetness of his wine, that he might have done it more wisely. He might have caught an outbound steamer and been well out of their clutches before now. But the other side of the world had seemed too far away and too uncertain then; he could not have waited for it; his need had been too sharp. If he had to choose over again, he would do the same thing tomorrow. He looked affectionately about the dining room, now gilded with a soft mist. Ah, it had paid indeed!

Paul was awakened next morning by a painful throbbing in his head and feet. He had thrown himself across the bed without undressing, and had slept with his shoes on. His limbs and hands were lead heavy, and his tongue and throat were parched. There came upon him one of those fateful attacks of clear-headedness that never occurred except when he was physically exhausted and his nerves hung loose. He lay still and closed his eyes and let the tide of realities wash over him.

His father was in New York; "stopping at some joint or other," he told himself. The memory of successive summers on the front stoop fell upon him like a weight of black water. He had not a hundred dollars left; and he knew now, more than ever, that money was everything, the wall that stood between all he loathed and all he wanted. The thing was winding itself up; he had thought of that on his first glorious day in New York, and had even provided a way to snap the thread. It lay on his dressing-table now; he had got it out last night when he came blindly up from dinner,—but the shiny metal hurt his eyes, and he disliked the look of it, anyway.

He rose and moved about with a painful effort, succumbing now and again to attacks of nausea. It was the old depression exaggerated; all the world had become Cordelia Street. Yet somehow he was not afraid of anything, was absolutely calm; perhaps because he had looked into the dark corner at last, and knew. It was bad enough, what he saw there; but somehow not so bad as his long fear of it had been. He saw everything clearly now. He had a feeling that he had made the best of it, that he had lived the sort of life he was meant to live, and for half an hour he sat staring at the revolver. But he told himself that was not the way, so he went downstairs and took a cab to the ferry.

When Paul arrived at Newark, he got off the train and took another cab, directing the driver to follow the Pennsylvania tracks out of the town. The snow lay heavy on the roadways and had drifted deep in the open fields. Only here and there the dead grass or dried weed stalks projected, singularly black, above it. Once well into the country, Paul dismissed the carriage and walked, floundering along the tracks, his mind a medley of irrelevant things. He seemed to hold in his brain an actual picture of everything he had seen that morning. He remembered every feature of both his drivers, the toothless old woman from whom he had bought the red flowers in his coat, the agent from whom he had got his ticket, and all of his fellow-passengers on the ferry. His mind, unable to cope with vital matters near at hand, worked feverishly and deftly at sorting and grouping these images. They made for him a part of the ugliness of the world, of the ache in his head, and the bitter burning on his tongue. He stooped and put a handful of snow into his mouth as he walked, but that, too, seemed hot. When he reached a little hillside, where the tracks ran through a cut some twenty feet below him, he stopped and sat down.

The carnations in his coat were drooping with the cold, he noticed; all their red glory over. It occurred to him that all the flowers he had seen in the show windows that first night must have gone the same way, long before this. It was only one splendid breath they had, in spite of their brave mockery at the winter outside the glass. It was a losing game in the end, it seemed, this revolt against the homilies by which the world is run. Paul took one of the blossoms carefully from his coat and scooped a little hole in the snow, where he covered it up. Then he dozed a while, from his weak condition, seeming insensible to the cold.

The sound of an approaching train woke him, and he started to his feet, remembering only his resolution, and afraid lest he should be too late. He stood watching the approaching locomotive, his teeth chattering, his lips drawn away from them in a frightened smile; once or twice he glanced nervously sidewise, as though he were being watched. When the right moment came, he jumped. As he fell, the folly of his haste occurred to him with merciless clearness, the vastness of what he had left undone. There flashed through his brain, clearer than ever before, the blue of Adriatic water, the yellow of Algerian sands.

He felt something strike his chest,—his body was being thrown swiftly through the air, on and on, immeasurably far and fast, while his limbs gently relaxed. Then, because the picture-making mechanism was crushed, the disturbing visions flashed into black, and Paul dropped back into the immense design of things.

D. H. LAWRENCE

# ❧ *The Rocking-Horse Winner*

THERE WAS a woman who was beautiful, who started with all the advantages, yet she had no luck. She married for love, and the love turned to dust. She had bonny children, yet she felt they had been thrust upon her, and she could not love them. They looked at her coldly, as if they were finding fault with her. And hurriedly she felt she must cover up some fault in herself. Yet what it was that she must cover up she never knew. Nevertheless, when her children were present, she always felt the center of her heart go hard. This troubled her, and in her manner she was all the more gentle and anxious for her children, as if she loved them very much. Only she herself knew that at the center of her heart was a hard little place that could not feel love, no, not for anybody. Everybody else said of her: "She is such a good mother. She adores her children." Only she herself, and her children themselves, knew it was not so. They read it in each other's eyes.

There were a boy and two little girls. They lived in a pleasant house, with a garden, and they had discreet servants, and felt themselves superior to anyone in the neighborhood.

Although they lived in style, they felt always an anxiety in the house. There was never enough money. The mother had a small income, and the father had a small income, but not nearly enough for the social position which they had to keep up. The father went into town to some office. But though he had good

62

prospects, these prospects never materialized. There was always the grinding sense of the shortage of money, though the style was always kept up.

At last the mother said: "I will see if *I* can't make something." But she did not know where to begin. She racked her brains, and tried this thing and the other, but could not find anything successful. The failure made deep lines come into her face. Her children were growing up, they would have to go to school. There must be more money, there must be more money. The father, who was always very handsome and expensive in his tastes, seemed as if he never *would* be able to do anything worth doing. And the mother, who had a great belief in herself, did not succeed any better, and her tastes were just as expensive.

And so the house came to be haunted by the unspoken phrase: *There must be more money! There must be more money!* The children could hear it all the time, though nobody said it aloud. They heard it at Christmas, when the expensive and splendid toys filled the nursery. Behind the shining modern rocking-horse, behind the smart doll's house, a voice would start whispering: "There *must* be more money! There *must* be more money!" And the children would stop playing, to listen for a moment. They would look into each other's eyes, to see if they had all heard. And each one saw in the eyes of the other two that they too had heard. "There *must* be more money! There *must* be more money!"

It came whispering from the springs of the still-swaying rocking-horse, and even the horse, bending his wooden, champing head, heard it. The big doll, sitting so pink and smirking in her new pram, could hear it quite plainly, and seemed to be smirking all the more self-consciously because of it. The foolish puppy, too, that took the place of the teddy-bear, he was looking so extraordinarily foolish for no other reason but that he heard the secret whisper all over the house: "There *must* be more money!"

Yet nobody ever said it aloud. The whisper was everywhere, and therefore no one spoke it. Just as no one ever says: "We are breathing!" in spite of the fact that breath is coming and going all the time.

"Mother," said the boy Paul one day, "why don't we keep a car of our own? Why do we always use uncle's, or else a taxi?"

"Because we're the poor members of the family," said the mother.

"But why *are* we, mother?"

"Well—I suppose," she said slowly and bitterly, "it's because your father has no luck."

The boy was silent for some time.

"Is luck money, mother?" he asked, rather timidly.

"No, Paul. Not quite. It's what causes you to have money."

"Oh!" said Paul vaguely. "I thought when Uncle Oscar said *filthy lucker*, it meant money."

"*Filthy lucre* does mean money," said the mother. "But it's lucre, not luck."

"Oh!" said the boy. "Then what *is* luck, mother?"

"It's what causes you to have money. If you're lucky you have money. That's why it's better to be born lucky than rich. If you're rich, you may lose your money. But if you're lucky, you will always get more money."

"Oh! Will you? And is father not lucky?"

"Very unlucky, I should say," she said bitterly.

The boy watched her with unsure eyes.

"Why?" he asked.

"I don't know. Nobody ever knows why one person is lucky and another unlucky."

"Don't they? Nobody at all? Does *nobody* know?"

"Perhaps God. But He never tells."

"He ought to, then. And aren't you lucky either, mother?"

"I can't be, if I married an unlucky husband."

"But by yourself, aren't you?"

"I used to think I was, before I married. Now I think I am very unlucky indeed."

"Why?"

"Well—never mind! Perhaps I'm not really," she said.

The child looked at her to see if she meant it. But he saw, by the lines of her mouth, that she was only trying to hide something from him.

"Well, anyhow," he said stoutly, "I'm a lucky person."

"Why?" said his mother, with a sudden laugh.

He stared at her. He didn't even know why he had said it.

"God told me," he asserted, brazening it out.

"I hope He did, dear!" she said, again with a laugh, but rather bitter.

"He did, mother!"

"Excellent!" said the mother, using one of her husband's exclamations.

The boy saw she did not believe him; or rather, that she paid no attention to his assertion. This angered him somewhat, and made him want to compel her attention.

He went off by himself, vaguely, in a childish way, seeking for the clue to "luck." Absorbed, taking no heed of other people, he went about with a sort of stealth, seeking inwardly for luck. He wanted luck, he wanted it, he wanted it. When the two girls were playing dolls in the nursery, he would sit on his big rocking-horse, charging madly into space, with a frenzy that made the little girls peer at him uneasily. Wildly the horse careered, the waving dark hair of the boy tossed, his eyes had a strange glare in them. The little girls dared not speak to him.

When he had ridden to the end of his mad little journey, he climbed down and stood in front of his rocking-horse, staring fixedly into its lowered face. Its red mouth was slightly open, its big eye was wide and glassy-bright.

"Now!" he would silently command the snorting steed. "Now, take me to where there is luck! Now take me!"

And he would slash the horse on the neck with the little whip he had asked

Uncle Oscar for. He *knew* the horse could take him to where there was luck, if only he forced it. So he would mount again and start on his furious ride, hoping at last to get there. He knew he could get there.

"You'll break your horse, Paul!" said the nurse.

"He's always riding like that! I wish he'd leave off!" said his elder sister Joan.

But he only glared down on them in silence. Nurse gave him up. She could make nothing of him. Anyhow, he was growing beyond her.

One day his mother and his Uncle Oscar came in when he was on one of his furious rides. He did not speak to them.

"Hallo, you young jockey! Riding a winner?" said his uncle.

"Aren't you growing too big for a rocking-horse? You're not a very little boy any longer, you know," said his mother.

But Paul only gave a blue glare from his big, rather close-set eyes. He would speak to nobody when he was in full tilt. His mother watched him with an anxious expression on her face.

At last he suddenly stopped forcing his horse into the mechanical gallop and slid down.

"Well, I got there!" he announced fiercely, his blue eyes still flaring, and his sturdy long legs straddling apart.

"Where did you get to?" asked his mother.

"Where I wanted to go," he flared back at her.

"That's right, son!" said Uncle Oscar. "Don't you stop till you get there. What's the horse's name?"

"He doesn't have a name," said the boy.

"Gets on without all right?" asked the uncle.

"Well, he has different names. He was called Sansovino last week."

"Sansovino, eh? Won the Ascot. How did you know his name?"

"He always talks about horse-races with Bassett," said Joan.

The uncle was delighted to find that his small nephew was posted with all the racing news. Bassett, the young gardener, who had been wounded in the left foot in the war and had got his present job through Oscar Cresswell, whose batman he had been, was a perfect blade of the "turf." He lived in the racing events, and the small boy lived with him.

Oscar Cresswell got it all from Bassett.

"Master Paul comes and asks me, so I can't do more than tell him, sir," said Bassett, his face terribly serious, as if he were speaking of religious matters.

"And does he ever put anything on a horse he fancies?"

"Well—I don't want to give him away—he's a young sport, a fine sport, sir. Would you mind asking him himself? He sort of takes a pleasure in it, and perhaps he'd feel I was giving him away, sir, if you don't mind."

Bassett was serious as a church.

The uncle went back to his nephew and took him off for a ride in the car.

"Say, Paul, old man, do you ever put anything on a horse?" the uncle asked.

The boy watched the handsome man closely.

"Why, do you think I oughtn't to?" he parried.

"Not a bit of it! I thought perhaps you might give me a tip for the Lincoln."

The car sped on into the country, going down to Uncle Oscar's place in Hampshire.

"Honor bright?" said the nephew.

"Honor bright, son!" said the uncle.

"Well, then, Daffodil."

"Daffodil! I doubt it, sonny. What about Mirza?"

"I only know the winner," said the boy. "That's Daffodil."

"Daffodil, eh?"

There was a pause. Daffodil was an obscure horse comparatively.

"Uncle!"

"Yes, son?"

"You won't let it go any further, will you? I promised Bassett."

"Bassett be damned, old man! What's he got to do with it?"

"We're partners. We've been partners from the first. Uncle, he lent me my first five shillings, which I lost. I promised him, honor bright, it was only between me and him; only you gave me that ten-shilling note I started winning with, so I thought you were lucky. You won't let it go any further, will you?"

The boy gazed at his uncle from those big, hot, blue eyes, set rather close together. The uncle stirred and laughed uneasily.

"Right you are, son! I'll keep your tip private. Daffodil, eh? How much are you putting on him?"

"All except twenty pounds," said the boy. "I keep that in reserve."

The uncle thought it a good joke.

"You keep twenty pounds in reserve, do you, you young romancer? What are you betting, then?"

"I'm betting three hundred," said the boy gravely. "But it's between you and me, Uncle Oscar! Honor bright?"

The uncle burst into a roar of laughter.

"It's between you and me all right, you young Nat Gould [a novelist who wrote 130 books about horse racing]," he said, laughing. "But where's your three hundred?"

"Bassett keeps it for me. We're partners."

"You are, are you! And what is Bassett putting on Daffodil?"

"He won't go quite as high as I do, I expect. Perhaps he'll go a hundred and fifty."

"What, pennies?" laughed the uncle.

"Pounds," said the child, with a surprised look at his uncle. "Bassett keeps a bigger reserve than I do."

Between wonder and amusement Uncle Oscar was silent. He pursued the matter no further, but he determined to take his nephew with him to the Lincoln races.

"Now, son," he said, "I'm putting twenty on Mirza, and I'll put five on for you on any horse you fancy. What's your pick?"

"Daffodil, uncle."

"No, not the fiver on Daffodil!"

"I should if it was my own fiver," said the child.

"Good! Good! Right you are! A fiver for me and a fiver for you on Daffodil."

The child had never been to a race-meeting before, and his eyes were blue fire. He pursed his mouth tight and watched. A Frenchman just in front had put his money on Lancelot. Wild with excitement, he flayed his arms up and down, yelling "*Lancelot! Lancelot!*" in his French accent.

Daffodil came in first, Lancelot second, Mirza third. The child, flushed and with eyes blazing, was curiously serene. His uncle brought him four five-pound notes, four to one.

"What am I to do with these?" he cried, waving them before the boy's eyes.

"I suppose we'll talk to Bassett," said the boy. "I expect I have fifteen hundred now; and twenty in reserve; and this twenty."

His uncle studied him for some moments.

"Look here, son!" he said. "You're not serious about Bassett and that fifteen hundred, are you?"

"Yes, I am. But it's between you and me, uncle. Honor bright?"

"Honor bright all right, son! But I must talk to Bassett."

"If you'd like to be a partner, uncle, with Bassett and me, we could all be partners. Only, you'd have to promise, honor bright, uncle, not to let it go beyond us three. Bassett and I are lucky, and you must be lucky, because it was your ten shillings I started winning with. . . ."

Uncle Oscar took both Bassett and Paul into Richmond Park for an afternoon, and there they talked.

"It's like this, you see, sir," Bassett said. "Master Paul would get me talking about racing events, spinning yarns, you know, sir. And he was always keen on knowing if I'd made or if I'd lost. It's about a year since, now, that I put five shillings on Blush of Dawn for him: and we lost. Then the luck turned, with that ten shillings he had from you: that we put on Singhalese. And since that time, it's been pretty steady, all things considering. What do you say, Master Paul?"

"We're all right when we're sure," said Paul. "It's when we're not quite sure that we go down."

"Oh, but we're careful then," said Bassett.

"But when are you *sure?*" smiled Uncle Oscar.

"It's Master Paul, sir," said Bassett in a secret, religious voice. "It's as if he had it from heaven. Like Daffodil, now, for the Lincoln. That was as sure as eggs."

"Did you put anything on Daffodil?" asked Oscar Cresswell.

"Yes, sir. I made my bit."

"And my nephew?"

Bassett was obstinately silent, looking at Paul.

"I made twelve hundred, didn't I, Bassett? I told uncle I was putting three hundred on Daffodil."

"That's right," said Bassett, nodding.

"But where's the money?" asked the uncle.

"I keep it safe locked up, sir. Master Paul he can have it any minute he likes to ask for it."

"What, fifteen hundred pounds?"

"And twenty! And *forty*, that is, with the twenty he made on the course."

"It's amazing!" said the uncle.

"If Master Paul offers you to be partners, sir, I would, if I were you: if you'll excuse me," said Bassett.

Oscar Cresswell thought about it.

"I'll see the money," he said.

They drove home again, and, sure enough, Bassett came round to the garden-house with fifteen hundred pounds in notes. The twenty pounds reserve was left with Joe Glee, in the Turf Commission deposit.

"You see, it's all right, uncle, when I'm *sure!* Then we go strong, for all we're worth. Don't we, Bassett?"

"We do that, Master Paul."

"And when are you sure?" said the uncle, laughing.

"Oh, well, sometimes I'm *absolutely* sure, like about Daffodil," said the boy; "and sometimes I have an idea; and sometimes I haven't even an idea, have I, Bassett? Then we're careful, because we mostly go down."

"You do, do you! And when you're sure, like about Daffodil, what makes you sure, sonny?"

"Oh, well, I don't know," said the boy uneasily. "I'm sure, you know, uncle; that's all."

"It's as if he had it from heaven, sir," Bassett reiterated.

"I should say so!" said the uncle.

But he became a partner. And when the Leger was coming on Paul was "sure" about Lively Spark, which was a quite inconsiderable horse. The boy insisted on putting a thousand on the horse, Bassett went for five hundred, and Oscar Cresswell two hundred. Lively Spark came in first, and the betting had been ten to one against him. Paul had made ten thousand.

"You see," he said, "I was absolutely sure of him."

Even Oscar Cresswell had cleared two thousand.

"Look here, son," he said, "this sort of thing makes me nervous."

"It needn't, uncle! Perhaps I shan't be sure again for a long time."

"But what are you going to do with your money?" asked the uncle.

"Of course," said the boy, "I started it for mother. She said she had no luck, because father is unlucky, so I thought if *I* was lucky, it might stop whispering."

"What might stop whispering?"

"Our house. I *hate* our house for whispering."

"What does it whisper?"

"Why—why"—the boy fidgeted—"why, I don't know. But it's always short of money, you know, uncle."

"I know it, son, I know it."

"You know people send mother writs, don't you, uncle?"

"I'm afraid I do," said the uncle.

"And then the house whispers, like people laughing at you behind your back. It's awful, that is! I thought if I was lucky—"

"You might stop it," added the uncle.

The boy watched him with big blue eyes, that had an uncanny cold fire in them, and he said never a word.

"Well, then!" said the uncle. "What are we doing?"

"I shouldn't like mother to know I was lucky," said the boy.

"Why not, son?"

"She'd stop me."

"I don't think she would."

"Oh!"—and the boy writhed in an odd way—"I *don't* want her to know, uncle."

"All right, son! We'll manage it without her knowing."

They managed it very easily. Paul, at the other's suggestion, handed over five thousand pounds to his uncle, who deposited it with the family lawyer, who was then to inform Paul's mother that a relative had put five thousand pounds into his hands, which sum was to be paid out a thousand pounds at a time, on the mother's birthday, for the next five years.

"So she'll have a birthday present of a thousand pounds for five successive years," said Uncle Oscar. "I hope it won't make it all the harder for her later."

Paul's mother had her birthday in November. The house had been "whispering" worse than ever lately, and, even in spite of his luck, Paul could not bear up against it. He was very anxious to see the effect of the birthday letter, telling his mother about the thousand pounds.

When there were no visitors, Paul now took his meals with his parents, as he was beyond the nursery control. His mother went into town nearly every day. She had discovered that she had an odd knack of sketching furs and dress materials, so she worked secretly in the studio of a friend who was the chief "artist" for the leading drapers. She drew the figures of ladies in furs and ladies in silk and sequins for the newspaper advertisements. This young woman artist earned several thousand pounds a year, but Paul's mother only made several hundreds, and she was again dissatisfied. She so wanted to be first in something, and she did not succeed, even in making sketches for drapery advertisements.

She was down to breakfast on the morning of her birthday. Paul watched her face as she read her letters. He knew the lawyer's letter. As his mother read it, her face hardened and became more expressionless. Then a cold, determined look came on her mouth. She hid the letter under the pile of others, and said not a word about it.

"Didn't you have anything nice in the post for your birthday, mother?" said Paul.

"Quite moderately nice," she said, her voice cold and absent.

She went away to town without saying more.

But in the afternoon Uncle Oscar appeared. He said Paul's mother had had a long interview with the lawyer, asking if the whole five thousand could not be advanced at once, as she was in debt.

"What do you think, uncle?" said the boy.

"I leave it to you, son."

"Oh, let her have it, then! We can get some more with the other," said the boy.

"A bird in the hand is worth two in the bush, laddie!" said Uncle Oscar.

"But I'm sure to *know* for the Grand National; or the Lincolnshire; or else the Derby. I'm sure to know for *one* of them," said Paul.

So Uncle Oscar signed the agreement, and Paul's mother touched the whole five thousand. Then something very curious happened. The voices in the house suddenly went mad, like a chorus of frogs on a spring evening. There were certain new furnishings, and Paul had a tutor. He was *really* going to Eton, his father's school, in the following autumn. There were flowers in the winter, and a blossoming of the luxury Paul's mother had been used to. And yet the voices in the house, behind the sprays of mimosa and almond-blossom, and from under the piles of iridescent cushions, simply trilled and screamed in a sort of ecstasy: "There *must* be more money! Oh-h-h; there *must* be more money. Oh, now, now-w! Now-w-w—there *must* be more money!—more than ever! More than ever!"

It frightened Paul terribly. He studied away at his Latin and Greek with his tutor. But his intense hours were spent with Bassett. The Grand National had gone by: he had not "known," and had lost a hundred pounds. Summer was at hand. He was in agony for the Lincoln. But even for the Lincoln he didn't "know," and he lost fifty pounds. He became wild-eyed and strange, as if something were going to explode in him.

"Let it alone, son! Don't you bother about it!" urged Uncle Oscar. But it was as if the boy couldn't really hear what his uncle was saying.

"I've got to know for the Derby! I've got to know for the Derby!" the child reiterated, his big blue eyes blazing with a sort of madness.

His mother noticed how overwrought he was.

"You'd better go to the seaside. Wouldn't you like to go now to the seaside, instead of waiting? I think you'd better," she said, looking down at him anxiously, her heart curiously heavy because of him.

But the child lifted his uncanny blue eyes.

"I couldn't possibly go before the Derby, mother!" he said. "I couldn't possibly!"

"Why not?" she said, her voice becoming heavy when she was opposed. "Why not? You can still go from the seaside to see the Derby with your Uncle Oscar, if that's what you wish. No need for you to wait here. Besides, I think you care too much about these races. It's a bad sign. My family has been a gambling family, and you won't know till you grow up how much damage it has done. But it has done damage. I shall have to send Bassett away, and ask Uncle Oscar not to talk racing to you, unless you promise to be reasonable about it: go away to the seaside and forget it. You're all nerves!"

"I'll do what you like, mother, so long as you don't send me away till after the Derby," the boy said.

"Send you away from where? Just from this house?"

"Yes," he said, gazing at her.

"Why, you curious child, what makes you care about this house so much, suddenly? I never knew you loved it."

He gazed at her without speaking. He had a secret within a secret, something he had not divulged, even to Bassett or to his Uncle Oscar.

But his mother, after standing undecided and a little bit sullen for some moments, said:

"Very well, then! Don't go to the seaside till after the Derby, if you don't wish it. But promise me you won't let your nerves go to pieces. Promise you won't think so much about horse-racing and *events*, as you call them!"

"Oh no," said the boy casually. "I won't think much about them, mother. You needn't worry. I wouldn't worry, mother, if I were you."

"If you were me and I were you," said his mother, "I wonder what we *should* do!"

"But you know you needn't worry, mother, don't you?" the boy repeated.

"I should be awfully glad to know it," she said wearily.

"Oh, well, you *can*, you know. I mean, you *ought* to know you needn't worry," he insisted.

"Ought I? Then I'll see about it," she said.

Paul's secret of secrets was his wooden horse, that which had no name. Since he was emancipated from a nurse and a nursery-governess, he had had his rocking-horse removed to his own bedroom at the top of the house.

"Surely you're too big for a rocking-horse!" his mother had remonstrated.

"Well, you see, mother, till I can have a *real* horse, I like to have *some* sort of animal about," had been his quaint answer.

"Do you feel he keeps you company?" she laughed.

"Oh yes! He's very good, he always keeps me company, when I'm there," said Paul.

So the horse, rather shabby, stood in an arrested prance in the boy's bedroom.

The Derby was drawing near, and the boy grew more and more tense. He hardly heard what was spoken to him, he was very frail, and his eyes were really uncanny. His mother had sudden strange seizures of uneasiness about him. Sometimes, for half an hour, she would feel a sudden anxiety about him that was almost anguish. She wanted to rush to him at once, and know he was safe.

Two nights before the Derby, she was at a big party in town, when one of her rushes of anxiety about her boy, her first-born, gripped her heart till she could hardly speak. She fought with the feeling, might and main, for she believed in common sense. But it was too strong. She had to leave the dance and go downstairs to telephone to the country. The children's nursery-governess was terribly surprised and startled at being rung up in the night.

"Are the children all right, Miss Wilmot?"

"Oh yes, they are quite all right."

"Master Paul? Is he all right?"

"He went to bed as right as a trivet. Shall I run up and look at him?"

"No," said Paul's mother reluctantly. "No! Don't trouble. It's all right. Don't sit up. We shall be home fairly soon." She did not want her son's privacy intruded upon.

"Very good," said the governess.

It was about one o'clock when Paul's mother and father drove up to their house. All was still. Paul's mother went to her room and slipped off her white fur cloak. She had told her maid not to wait up for her. She heard her husband downstairs, mixing a whisky and soda.

And then, because of the strange anxiety at her heart, she stole upstairs to her son's room. Noiselessly she went along the upper corridor. Was there a faint noise? What was it?

She stood, with arrested muscles, outside his door, listening. There was a strange, heavy, and yet not loud noise. Her heart stood still. It was a soundless noise, yet rushing and powerful. Something huge, in violent, hushed motion. What was it? What in God's name was it? She ought to know. She felt that she knew the noise. She knew what it was.

Yet she could not place it. She couldn't say what it was. And on and on it went, like a madness.

Softly, frozen with anxiety and fear, she turned the doorhandle.

The room was dark. Yet in the space near the window, she heard and saw something plunging to and fro. She gazed in fear and amazement.

Then suddenly she switched on the light, and saw her son, in his green pyjamas, madly surging on the rocking-horse. The blaze of light suddenly lit him up, as he urged the wooden horse, and lit her up, as she stood, blonde, in her dress of pale green and crystal, in the doorway.

"Paul!" she cried. "Whatever are you doing?"

"It's Malabar!" he screamed in a powerful, strange voice. "It's Malabar!"

His eyes blazed at her for one strange and senseless second, as he ceased urging his wooden horse. Then he fell with a crash to the ground, and she, all her tormented motherhood flooding upon her, rushed to gather him up.

But he was unconscious, and unconscious he remained, with some brain-fever. He talked and tossed, and his mother sat stonily by his side.

"Malabar! It's Malabar! Bassett, Bassett, I *know*! It's Malabar!"

So the child cried, trying to get up and urge the rocking-horse that gave him his inspiration.

"What does he mean by Malabar?" asked the heart-frozen mother.

"I don't know," said the father stonily.

"What does he mean by Malabar?" she asked her brother Oscar.

"It's one of the horses running for the Derby," was the answer.

And, in spite of himself, Oscar Cresswell spoke to Bassett, and himself put a thousand on Malabar: at fourteen to one.

The third day of the illness was critical: they were waiting for a change. The boy, with his rather long, curly hair, was tossing ceaselessly on the pillow. He neither slept nor regained consciousness, and his eyes were like blue stones. His mother sat, feeling her heart had gone, turned actually into a stone.

In the evening, Oscar Cresswell did not come, but Bassett sent a message, saying could he come up for one moment, just one moment? Paul's mother was very angry at the intrusion, but on second thought she agreed. The boy was the same. Perhaps Bassett might bring him to consciousness.

The gardener, a shortish fellow with a little brown moustache and sharp little brown eyes, tiptoed into the room, touched his imaginary cap to Paul's mother, and stole to the bedside, staring with glittering, smallish eyes at the tossing, dying child.

"Master Paul!" he whispered. "Master Paul! Malabar came in first all right, a clean win. I did as you told me. You've made over seventy thousand pounds, you have; you've got over eighty thousand. Malabar came in all right, Master Paul."

"Malabar! Malabar! Did I say Malabar, mother? Did I say Malabar? Do you think I'm lucky, mother? I knew Malabar, didn't I? Over eighty thousand pounds! I call that lucky, don't you, mother? Over eighty thousand pounds! I knew, didn't I know I knew? Malabar came in all right. If I ride my horse till I'm sure, then I tell you, Bassett, you can go as high as you like. Did you go for all you were worth, Bassett?"

"I went a thousand on it, Master Paul."

"I never told you, mother, that if I can ride my horse, and *get there*, then I'm absolutely sure—oh, absolutely! Mother, did I ever tell you? I *am* lucky!"

"No, you never did," said his mother.

But the boy died in the night.

And even as he lay dead, his mother heard her brother's voice saying to her: "My God, Hester, you're eighty-odd thousand to the good, and a poor devil of a son to the bad. But, poor devil, poor devil, he's best gone out of a life where he rides his rocking-horse to find a winner."

# ✤ The Killers

THE DOOR of Henry's lunchroom opened and two men came in. They sat down at the counter.

"What's yours?" George asked them.

"I don't know," one of the men said. "What do you want to eat, Al?"

"I don't know," said Al. "I don't know what I want to eat."

Outside it was getting dark. The street-light came on outside the window. The two men at the counter read the menu. From the other end of the counter Nick Adams watched them. He had been talking to George when they came in.

"I'll have a roast pork tenderloin with apple sauce and mashed potatoes," the first man said.

"It isn't ready yet."

"What the hell do you put it on the card for?"

"That's the dinner," George explained. "You can get that at six o'clock."

George looked at the clock on the wall behind the counter.

"It's five o'clock."

"The clock says twenty minutes past five," the second man said.

"It's twenty minutes fast."

"Oh, to hell with the clock," the first man said. "What have you got to eat?"

"I can give you any kind of sandwiches," George said. "You can have ham and eggs, bacon and eggs, liver and bacon, or a steak."

"Give me chicken croquettes with green peas and cream sauce and mashed potatoes."

"That's the dinner."

"Everything we want's the dinner, eh? That's the way you work it."

"I can give you ham and eggs, bacon and eggs, liver—"

"I'll take ham and eggs," the man called Al said. He wore a derby hat and a black overcoat buttoned across the chest. His face was small and white and he had tight lips. He wore a silk muffler and gloves.

"Give me bacon and eggs," said the other man. He was about the same size as Al. Their faces were different, but they were dressed like twins. Both wore overcoats too tight for them. They sat leaning forward, their elbows on the counter.

"Got anything to drink?" Al asked.

"Silver beer, bevo, ginger-ale," George said.

"I mean you got anything to *drink?*"

74

"Just those I said."

"This is a hot town," said the other. "What do they call it?"

"Summit."

"Ever hear of it?" Al asked his friend.

"No," said the friend.

"What do you do here nights?" Al asked.

"They eat the dinner," his friend said. "They all come here and eat the big dinner."

"That's right," George said.

"So you think that's right?" Al asked George.

"Sure."

"You're a pretty bright boy, aren't you?"

"Sure," said George.

"Well, you're not," said the other little man. "Is he, Al?"

"He's dumb," said Al. He turned to Nick. "What's your name?"

"Adams."

"Another bright boy," Al said. "Ain't he a bright boy, Max?"

"The town's full of bright boys," Max said.

George put the two platters, one of ham and eggs, the other of bacon and eggs, on the counter. He set down two side-dishes of fried potatoes and closed the wicket into the kitchen.

"Which is yours?" he asked Al.

"Don't you remember?"

"Ham and eggs."

"Just a bright boy," Max said. He leaned forward and took the ham and eggs. Both men ate with their gloves on. George watched them eat.

"What are *you* looking at?" Max looked at George.

"Nothing."

"The hell you were. You were looking at me."

"Maybe the boy meant it for a joke, Max," Al said.

George laughed.

"*You* don't have to laugh," Max said to him. "*You* don't have to laugh at all, see?"

"All right," said George.

"So he thinks it's all right." Max turned to Al. "He thinks it's all right. That's a good one."

"Oh, he's a thinker," Al said. They went on eating.

"What's the bright boy's name down the counter?" Al asked Max.

"Hey, bright boy," Max said to Nick. "You go around on the other side of the counter with your boy friend."

"What's the idea?" Nick asked.

"There isn't any idea."

"You better go around, bright boy," Al said. Nick went around behind the counter.

"What's the idea?" George asked.

"None of your damn business," Al said. "Who's out in the kitchen?"

"The nigger."

"What do you mean the nigger?"

"The nigger that cooks."

"Tell him to come in."

"What's the idea?"

"Tell him to come in."

"Where do you think you are?"

"We know damn well where we are," the man called Max said. "Do we look silly?"

"You talk silly," Al said to him. "What the hell do you argue with this kid for? Listen," he said to George, "tell the nigger to come out here."

"What are you going to do to him?"

"Nothing. Use your head, bright boy. What would we do to a nigger?"

George opened the slit that opened back into the kitchen. "Sam," he called. "Come in here a minute."

The door to the kitchen opened and the nigger came in. "What was it?" he asked. The two men at the counter took a look at him.

"All right, nigger. You stand right there," Al said.

Sam, the nigger, standing in his apron, looked at the two men sitting at the counter. "Yes, sir," he said. Al got down from his stool.

"I'm going back to the kitchen with the nigger and bright boy," he said. "Go on back to the kitchen, nigger. You go with him, bright boy." The little man walked after Nick and Sam, the cook, back into the kitchen. The door shut after them. The man called Max sat at the counter opposite George. He didn't look at George but looked in the mirror that ran along back of the counter. Henry's had been made over from a saloon into a lunch counter.

"Well, bright boy," Max said, looking into the mirror, "why don't you say something?"

"What's it all about?"

"Hey, Al," Max called, "bright boy wants to know what it's all about."

"Why don't you tell him?" Al's voice came from the kitchen.

"What do you think it's all about?"

"I don't know."

"What do you think?"

Max looked into the mirror all the time he was talking.

"I wouldn't say."

"Hey, Al, bright boy says he wouldn't say what he thinks it's all about."

"I can hear you, all right," Al said from the kitchen. He had propped open the slit that dishes passed through into the kitchen with a catsup bottle. "Listen, bright boy," he said from the kitchen to George. "Stand a little further along the bar. You move a little to the left, Max." He was like a photographer arranging for a group picture.

"Talk to me, bright boy," Max said. "What do you think's going to happen?"

George did not say anything.

"I'll tell you," Max said. "We're going to kill a Swede. Do you know a big Swede named Ole Andreson?"

"Yes."

"He comes here to eat every night, don't he?"

"Sometimes he comes here."

"He comes here at six o'clock, don't he?"

"If he comes."

"We know all that, bright boy," Max said. "Talk about something else. Ever go to the movies?"

"Once in a while."

"You ought to go to the movies more. The movies are fine for a bright boy like you."

"What are you going to kill Ole Andreson for? What did he ever do to you?"

"He never had a chance to do anything to us. He never even seen us."

"And he's only going to see us once," Al said from the kitchen.

"What are you going to kill him for, then?" George asked.

"We're killing him for a friend. Just to oblige a friend, bright boy."

"Shut up," said Al from the kitchen. "You talk too goddam much."

"Well, I got to keep bright boy amused. Don't I, bright boy?"

"You talk too damn much," Al said. "The nigger and my bright boy are amused by themselves. I got them tied up like a couple of girl friends in the convent."

"I suppose you were in a convent."

"You never know."

"You were in a kosher convent. That's where you were."

George looked up at the clock.

"If anybody comes in you tell them the cook is off, and if they keep after it, you tell them you'll go back and cook yourself. Do you get that, bright boy?"

"All right," George said. "What you going to do with us afterward?"

"That'll depend," Max said. "That's one of those things you never know at the time."

George looked up at the clock. It was a quarter past six. The door from the street opened. A street-car motorman came in.

"Hello, George," he said. "Can I get supper?"

"Sam's gone out," George said. "He'll be back in about half an hour."

"I'd better go up the street," the motorman said. George looked at the clock. It was twenty minutes past six.

"That was nice, bright boy," Max said. "You're a regular little gentleman."

"He knew I'd blow his head off," Al said from the kitchen.

"No," said Max. "It ain't that. Bright boy is nice. He's a nice boy. I like him."

At six-fifty-five George said: "He's not coming."

Two other people had been in the lunch-room. Once George had gone out to the kitchen and made a ham-and-egg sandwich "to go" that a man wanted to take with him. Inside the kitchen he saw Al, his derby hat tipped back, sitting on a stool beside the wicket with the muzzle of a sawed-off shotgun resting on the ledge. Nick and the cook were back to back in the corner, a towel tied in each of their mouths. George had cooked the sandwich, wrapped it up in oiled paper, put it in a bag, brought it in, and the man had paid for it and gone out.

"Bright boy can do everything." Max said. "He can cook and everything. You'd make some girl a nice wife, bright boy."

"Yes?" George said. "Your friend, Ole Andreson, isn't going to come."

"We'll give him ten minutes," Max said.

Max watched the mirror and the clock. The hands of the clock marked seven o'clock, and then five minutes past seven.

"Come on, Al," said Max. "We better go. He's not coming."

"Better give him five minutes," Al said from the kitchen.

In the five minutes a man came in, and George explained that the cook was sick.

"Why the hell don't you get another cook?" the man asked. "Aren't you running a lunch-counter?" He went out.

"Come on, Al," Max said.

"What about the two bright boys and the nigger?"

"They're all right."

"You think so?"

"Sure. We're through with it."

"I don't like it," said Al. "It's sloppy. You talk too much."

"Oh, what the hell," said Max. "We got to keep amused, haven't we?"

"You talk too much, all the same," Al said. He came out from the kitchen. The cut-off barrels of the shotgun made a slight bulge under the waist of his too tight-fitting overcoat. He straightened his coat with his gloved hands.

"So long, bright boy," he said to George. "You got a lot of luck."

"That's the truth," Max said. "You ought to play the races, bright boy."

The two of them went out the door. George watched them, through the window, pass under the arc-light and across the street. In their tight overcoats and derby hats they looked like a vaudeville team. George went back through the swinging door into the kitchen and untied Nick and the cook.

"I don't want any more of that," said Sam, the cook, "I don't want any more of that."

Nick stood up. He had never had a towel in his mouth before. "Say," he said. "What the hell?" He was trying to swagger it off.

"They were going to kill Ole Andreson," George said. "They were going to shoot him when he came in to eat."

"Ole Andreson?"

"Sure."

The cook felt the corners of his mouth with his thumbs.

"They all gone?" he asked.

"Yeah," said George. "They're gone now."

"I don't like it," said the cook. "I don't like any of it at all."

"Listen," George said to Nick. "You better go see Ole Andreson."

"All right."

"You better not have anything to do with it at all," Sam, the cook, said. "You better stay way out of it."

"Don't go if you don't want to," George said.

"Mixing up in this ain't going to get you anywhere," the cook said. "You stay out of it."

"I'll go see him," Nick said to George. "Where does he live?" The cook turned away.

"Little boys always know what they want to do," he said.

"He lives up at Hirsch's rooming-house," George said to Nick.

"I'll go up there."

Outside the arc-light shone through the bare branches of a tree. Nick walked up the street beside the car-tracks and turned at the next arc-light down a side-street. Three houses up the street was Hirsch's rooming-house. Nick walked up the two steps and pushed the bell. A woman came to the door.

"Is Ole Andreson here?"

"Do you want to see him?"

"Yes, if he's in."

Nick followed the woman up a flight of stairs and back to the end of a corridor. She knocked on the door.

"Who is it?"

"It's somebody to see you, Mr. Andreson," the woman said.

"It's Nick Adams."

"Come in."

Nick opened the door and went into the room. Ole Andreson was lying on the bed with all his clothes on. He had been a heavyweight prizefighter and he was too long for the bed. He lay with his head on two pillows. He did not look at Nick.

"What was it?" he asked.

"I was up at Henry's," Nick said, "and two fellows came in and tied up me and the cook, and they said they were going to kill you."

It sounded silly when he said it. Ole Andreson said nothing.

"They put us out in the kitchen," Nick went on. "They were going to shoot you when you came in to supper."

Ole Andreson looked at the wall and did not say anything.

"George thought I better come and tell you about it."

"There isn't anything I can do about it," Ole Andreson said.

"I'll tell you what they were like,"

"I don't want to know what they were like," Ole Andreson said. He looked at the wall. "Thanks for coming to tell me about it."

"That's all right."

Nick looked at the big man lying on the bed.

"Don't you want me to go and see the police?"

"No," Ole Andreson said. "That wouldn't do any good."

"Isn't there something I could do?"

"No. There ain't anything to do."

"Maybe it was just a bluff."

"No. It ain't just a bluff."

Ole Andreson rolled over toward the wall.

"The only thing is," he said, talking toward the wall, "I just can't make up my mind to go out. I been in here all day."

"Couldn't you get out of town?"

"No," Ole Andreson said. "I'm through with all that running around."

He looked at the wall.

"There ain't anything to do now."

"Couldn't you fix it up some way?"

"No, I got in wrong." He talked in the same flat voice. "There ain't anything to do. After a while I'll make up my mind to go out."

"I better go back and see George," Nick said.

"So long," said Ole Andreson. He did not look toward Nick. "Thanks for coming around."

Nick went out. As he shut the door he saw Ole Andreson with all his clothes on, lying on the bed looking at the wall.

"He's been in his room all day," the landlady said downstairs. "I guess he don't feel well. I said to him: 'Mr. Andreson, you ought to go out and take a walk on a nice fall day like this,' but he didn't feel like it."

"He doesn't want to go out."

"I'm sorry he don't feel well," the woman said. "He's an awfully nice man. He was in the ring, you know."

"I know it."

"You'd never know it except from the way his face is," the woman said. They stood talking just inside the street door. "He's just as gentle."

"Well, good night, Mrs. Hirsch," Nick said.

"I'm not Mrs. Hirsch," the woman said. "She owns the place. I just look after it for her. I'm Mrs. Bell."

"Well, good night, Mrs. Bell," Nick said.

"Good night," the woman said.

Nick walked up the dark street to the corner under the arc-light, and then along the car-tracks to Henry's eating-house. George was inside, back of the counter. "Did you see Ole?"

"Yes," said Nick. "He's in his room and he won't go out."

The cook opened the door from the kitchen when he heard Nick's voice.

"I don't even listen to it," he said and shut the door.

"Did you tell him about it?" George asked.

"Sure. I told him but he knows what it's all about."

"What's he going to do?"

"Nothing."

"They'll kill him."

"I guess they will."

"He must have got mixed up in something in Chicago."

"I guess so," said Nick.

"It's a hell of a thing."

"It's an awful thing," Nick said.

They did not say anything. George reached down for a towel and wiped the counter.

"I wonder what he did?" Nick said.

"Double-crossed somebody. That's what they kill them for."

"I'm going to get out of this town," Nick said.

"Yes," said George. "That's a good thing to do."

"I can't stand to think about him waiting in the room and knowing he's going to get it. It's too damned awful."

"Well," said George, "you better not think about it."

KATHERINE ANNE PORTER

# ❧ *The Circus*

THE long planks set on trestles rose one above the other to a monstrous height and stretched dizzyingly in a wide oval ring. They were packed with people—"lak fleas on a dog's ear," said Dicey, holding Miranda's hand firmly and looking about her with disapproval. The white billows of enormous canvas sagged overhead, held up by three poles set evenly apart down the center. The family, when seated, occupied almost a whole section on one level.

On one side of them in a long row sat Father, sister Maria, brother Paul, Grandmother; great-aunt Keziah, cousin Keziah, and second-cousin Keziah, who had just come down from Kentucky on a visit; uncle Charles Breaux, cousin Charles Breaux, and aunt Marie-Anne Breaux. On the other side sat small cousin Lucie Breaux, big cousin Paul Gay, great-aunt Sally Gay (who took snuff and was therefore a disgrace to the family); two strange, extremely handsome young men who might be cousins but who were certainly in love with cousin Miranda Gay; and cousin Miranda Gay herself, a most dashing young lady with crisp silk skirts, a half dozen of them at once, a lovely perfume and wonderful black curly hair above enormous wild gray eyes, "like a colt's," Father said. Miranda hoped to be exactly like her when she grew up. Hanging to Dicey's arm she leaned out and waved to cousin Miranda, who waved back smiling, and the strange young men waved to her also. Miranda was most fearfully excited. It was her first circus; it might also be her last because the whole family had combined to persuade Grandmother to allow her to come with them. "Very well, this once," Grandmother said, "since it's a family reunion."

This once! This once! She could not look hard enough at everything. She even peeped down between the wide crevices of the piled-up plank seats, where she was astonished to see odd-looking, roughly dressed little boys peeping up from the dust below. They were squatted in little heaps, staring up quietly. She looked squarely into the eyes of one, who returned her a look so peculiar she gazed and gazed, trying to understand it. It was a bold grinning stare without any kind of friendliness in it. He was a thin, dirty little boy with a floppy old checkerboard cap pulled over crumpled red ears and dust-colored hair. As she gazed he nudged the little boy next to him, whispered, and the second little boy caught her eye. This was too much. Miranda pulled Dicey's sleeve. "Dicey, what are those little boys doing down there?" "Down where?" asked Dicey, but she seemed to know already, for she bent over and looked through the crevice, drew her knees together and her skirts around her, and said severely: "You jus mind yo' own business and stop throwin' yo' legs around that way. Don't you pay any mind. Plenty o' monkeys right here in the show widout you studyin dat kind."

An enormous brass band seemed to explode right at Miranda's ear. She jumped, quivered, thrilled blindly and almost forgot to breathe as sound and color and smell rushed together and poured through her skin and hair and beat in her head and hands and feet and pit of her stomach. "Oh," she called out in her panic, closing her eyes and seizing Dicey's hand hard. The flaring lights burned through her lids, a roar of laughter like rage drowned out the steady raging of the drums and horns. She opened her eyes . . . A creature in a blousy white overall with ruffles at the neck and ankles, with bone-white skull and chalk-white face, with tufted eyebrows far apart in the middle of his forehead, the lids in a black sharp angle, a long scarlet mouth stretching back into sunken cheeks, turned up at the corners in a perpetual bitter grimace of pain, astonishment, not smiling, pranced along a wire stretched down the center of the ring, balancing a long thin pole with little wheels at either end. Miranda thought at first he was walking on air, or flying, and this did not surprise her; but when she saw the wire, she was terrified. High above their heads the inhuman figure pranced, spinning the little wheels. He paused, slipped, the flapping white leg waved in space; he staggered, wobbled, slipped sidewise, plunged, and caught the wire with frantic knee, hanging there upside down, the other leg waving like a feeler above his head; slipped once more, caught by one frenzied heel, and swung back and forth like a scarf. . . . The crowd roared with savage delight, shrieks of dreadful laughter like devils in delicious torment. . . . Miranda shrieked too, with real pain, clutching at her stomach with her knees drawn up. . . . The man on the wire, hanging by his foot, turned his head like a seal from side to side and blew sneering kisses from his cruel mouth. Then Miranda covered her eyes and screamed, the tears pouring over her cheeks and chin.

"Take her home," said her father, "get her out of here at once," but the laughter was not wiped from his face. He merely glanced at her and back to the ring. "Take her away, Dicey," called the Grandmother, from under her half-raised crepe veil. Dicey, rebelliously, very slowly, without taking her gaze from the white figure swaying on the wire, rose, seized the limp, suffering bundle, prodded and lumped her way over knees and feet, through the crowd, down the levels of the scaffolding, across a space of sandy tanbark, out through a flap in the tent. Miranda was crying steadily with an occasional hiccough. A dwarf was standing in the entrance, wearing a little woolly beard, a pointed cap, tight red breeches, long shoes with turned-up toes. He carried a thin white wand. Miranda almost touched him before she saw him, her distorted face with its open mouth and glistening tears almost level with his. He leaned forward and peered at her with kind, not-human golden eyes, like a near-sighted dog: then made a horrid grimace at her, imitating her own face. Miranda struck at him in sheer ill temper, screaming. Dicey drew her away quickly, but not before Miranda had seen in his face, suddenly, a look of haughty, remote displeasure, a true grown-up look. She knew it well. It chilled her with a new kind of fear: she had not believed he was really human.

"Raincheck, get your raincheck!" said a very disagreeable-looking fellow as they passed. Dicey turned toward him almost in tears herself. "Mister, caint you see I won't be able to git back? I got this young un to see to. . . . What good dat lil piece of paper goin to do *me?*" All the way home she was cross, and grumbled under her breath: little ole meany . . . little ole scare-cat . . . gret big baby . . . never go nowhere . . . never see nothin . . . come on here now, hurry up—always ruinin everything for othah folks . . . won't let anybody rest a minute, won't let anybody have any good times . . . come on here now, you wanted to go home and you're going there . . . snatching Miranda along, vicious but cautious, careful not to cross the line where Miranda could say outright: "Dicey did this or said this to me . . ." Dicey was allowed a certain freedom up to a point.

The family trooped into the house just before dark and scattered out all over it. From every room came the sound of chatter and laughter. The other children told Miranda what she had missed: wonderful little ponies with plumes and bells on their bridles, ridden by darling little monkeys in velvet jackets and peaked hats . . . trained white goats that danced . . . a baby elephant that crossed his front feet and leaned against his cage and opened his mouth to bc fed, *such* a baby! . . . more clowns, funnier than the first one even . . . beautiful ladies with bright yellow hair, wearing white silk tights with red satin sashes, had performed on white trapezes; they also had hung by their toes, but how gracefully, like flying birds! Huge white horses had lolloped around and round the ring with men and women dancing on their backs! One man had swung by his teeth from the top of the tent and another had put his head in a lion's mouth. Ah, what she had not missed! Everybody had been enjoying themselves while she was missing her first big circus and spoiling the day for Dicey. Poor Dicey. Poor dear Dicey. The other children who hadn't thought of Dicey until that moment, mourned over her with sad mouths, their malicious eyes watching Miranda squirm. Dicey had been looking forward for weeks to this day! And then Miranda must get scared—"Can you *imagine* being afraid of that funny old clown?" each one asked the other, and then they smiled pityingly on Miranda. . . .

Then too, it had been a very important occasion in another way: it was the first time Grandmother had ever allowed herself to be persuaded to go to the circus. One could not gather, from her rather generalized opinions, whether there had been no circuses when she was young, or there had been and it was not proper to see them. At any rate for her usual sound reasons, Grandmother had never approved of circuses, and though she would not deny she had been amused somewhat, still there had been sights and sounds in this one which she maintained were, to say the least, not particularly edifying to the young. Her son Harry, who came in while the children made an early supper, looked at their illuminated faces, all the brothers and sisters and visiting cousins, and said, "This basket of young doesn't seem too much damaged." His mother said, "The fruits of their present are in a future so far off, neither of us may live to know whether harm has been done or not. That is the trouble," and she went on ladling out hot milk to pour over their buttered toast. Miranda was sitting silent, her underlip drooping. Her father smiled at her. "You missed it, Baby," he said softly, "and what good did that do you?"

Miranda burst again into tears: had to be taken away at last, and her supper was brought up to her. Dicey was exasperated and silent. Miranda could not eat. She tried, as if she were really remembering them, to think of the beautiful wild beings in white satin and spangles and red sashes who danced and frolicked on the trapezes; of the sweet little furry ponies and the lovely pet monkeys in their comical clothes. She fell asleep, and her invented memories gave way before her real ones, the bitter terrified face of the man in blowsy white falling to his death—ah, the cruel joke!—and the terrible grimace of the unsmiling dwarf. She screamed in her sleep and sat up crying for deliverance from her torments.

Dicey came, her cross, sleepy eyes half-closed, her big dark mouth pouted, thumping the floor with her thick bare feet. "I *swear*," she said, in a violent hoarse whisper. "What the matter with you? You need a good spankin, I *swear*! Wakin everybody up like this . . ."

Miranda was completely subjugated by her fears. She had a way of answering Dicey back. She would say, "Oh, hush up, Dicey." Or she would say, "I don't have to mind *you*. I don't have to mind anybody but my grandmother," which was provokingly true. And she would say, "You don't know what you're talking about." The day just past had changed that. Miranda sincerely did not want anybody, not even Dicey, to be cross with her. Ordinarily she did not care how cross she made the harassed adults around her. Now if Dicey must be cross, she still did not really care, if only Dicey might not turn out the lights and leave her to the fathomless terrors of the darkness where sleep could overtake her once more. She hugged Dicey with both arms, crying, "Don't, don't leave me. *Don't* be so angry! I c-c-can't b-bear it!"

Dicey lay down beside her with a long moaning sigh, which meant that she was collecting her patience and making up her mind to remember that she was a Christian and must bear her cross. "Now you go to sleep," she said, in her usual warm being-good voice. "Now you jes shut yo eyes and go to sleep. I ain't going to leave you. Dicey ain't mad at nobody . . . *nobody* in the whole worl'. . . ."

# Supplementary Reading List of Stories

Edgar Allan Poe: *The Black Cat*
Nathaniel Hawthorne: *Young Goodman Brown*
Herman Melville: *Bartleby the Scrivener*
Guy de Maupassant: *La Mère Sauvage*
Joseph Conrad: *The Lagoon*
Anton Chekhov: *The Lady with the Dog*
James Joyce: *The Boarding House*
Katherine Mansfield: *The Doll's House*
F. Scott Fitzgerald: *The Ice Palace*
William Faulkner: *A Rose for Emily*
John Steinbeck: *The Great Mountains*
Albert Camus: *The Guest*
J. F. Powers: *Zeal*
Truman Capote: *A Tree of Night*
Flannery O'Connor: *A Late Encounter with the Enemy*
John Updike: *Pigeon Feathers*

Reprinted in *An Introduction to Literature*, The World Publishing Company, 1966, edited by Ralph H. Singleton and Stanton Millet

# Biographies

ANDERSON, SHERWOOD (1876–1941), ashamed of his father's aimless career, established himself in business, successfully managing a paint factory and later writing for an advertising firm. When he came to view this kind of writing as prostitution of his talents, he turned to prose fiction. The psychological penetration into small town life and the experimental techniques in *Winesburg, Ohio* (1919), first attracted the critics. Although he excels in the short story, he also wrote novels, poetry, and his own memoirs.

CAMUS, ALBERT (1913–1960) did not leave his native Algiers until 1940, at which time, in the face of German occupation, he founded the secret resistance newspaper, *Combat*. The paper remained a powerful voice even after the liberation, and its editor assumed the leadership of the younger writers. His best novel, *The Stranger* (1942), appeared shortly before *The Myth of Sisyphus* (1942), his analysis of the absurdity in human life. Despite the negativism prevalent in his literary works, Camus took a positive position in support of political integrity and social justice. He won the Nobel Prize for Literature in 1957.

CAPOTE, TRUMAN (1924–    ) spent a difficult childhood in the deep South and turned early to writing. Winning a writing contest while still in grammar school brought him early notoriety, because his entry included recognizable portraiture of the townspeople. The appearance of "Miriam" in 1945 caused a more promising stir: eight publishers bid for his future work. With the publication of his first novel, *Other Voices, Other Rooms* (1948), he found himself a literary celebrity. *In Cold Blood* (1966), a "novel of fact," dealing with the murder of an entire family, is his latest success.

CATHER, WILLA (1873–1947) worked as a journalist, a high school teacher, and managing editor of *McClure's*, the leading contemporary "muckraking" magazine; but her youth, spent among immigrant families of Nebraska, bears most importantly on her best work. The significance of the land itself becomes increasingly central to her novels, especially in its effects on the artist, who is generally the outstanding figure in her books. Her best novels include *My Antonia* (1918) and *Death Comes for the Archbishop* (1927). Her first collection of short stories, *The Troll Garden*, appeared in 1905. *Not Under Forty* (1936) contains essays revealing her theory of fiction. She won the Pulitzer Prize in 1922.

CHEKHOV, ANTON PAVLOVICH (1860–1904) supported his destitute family and put himself through medical school as a hackwriter. As his creativity developed so did his passion for writing, until he admitted, "medicine is my lawful wife and literature is my mistress." Chekhov peoples his works with representatives of the Russian middle class; he reveals their ordinary, even stagnant, lives with honesty, humor, and sympathy. He was a successful dramatist and novelist, but his command of the short story—his stories have had a most significant influence on modern short-story writers—has marked him as a master of the form.

CONRAD, JOSEPH (Teodor Jozef Konrad Korzeniowski [1857–1924]), the son of Polish exiles, spent nearly twenty years at sea until disease contracted in the Congo prevented further travel. Theorists claim his career at sea was an escape from the duty of battling Czarist forces in Poland and that the escape settled deep feelings of guilt in him. His own demands for perfection compounded the difficulty of writing in a foreign language. Conrad, the master of the sea story, uses the sea as a means for setting characters in isolation. His concern "has been the ideal value of things, events, and people." Outstanding novels include *The Nigger of the Narcissus* (1898) and *Lord Jim* (1900). He also published numerous short stories; some of the best-known are "The Lagoon," "Heart of Darkness," and "The Secret Sharer."

FAULKNER, WILLIAM (1897–1963), novelist and sometime poet and short-story writer, created a mythical area in the South with its own particular heritage. Yoknapatawpha County, Mississippi, Faulkner's mythic setting, suggests a lazy surface—the cover for biracial tensions and the clashing interests of decadent and opposing modes of life seething below it (*The Sound and the Fury*, 1929; *As I Lay Dying*, 1930; and *Sartoris*, 1929). His exposures of violence, brutality, and perversion kept many from a serious appraisal of his work. Twice his novels were awarded the Pulitzer Prize. In 1950 he became the fourth American to receive the Nobel Prize for Literature. He summarized his own intention in saying, "the poet's voice need not merely be the record of man, it can be one of the props, the pillars to help him endure and prevail."

FITZGERALD, FRANCIS SCOTT KEY (1896–1940), chronicler of the Jazz Age, left in his novels, stories, and sketches the record of "a whole race gone hedonistic." His first novel, *This Side of Paradise* (1920), made him a success at twenty-three; the consequence was a lifetime of unsuccessful resistance to the temptations money offered. Ironically, his best work shatters the belief that wealth makes happiness. His reputation as an artist lies in his powerful novel, *The Great Gatsby* (1925), and in a few short stories. His literary reputation was restored in the late 1940's and early 1950's by the efforts of critics and friends, most notably Edmund Wilson, who compiled an autobiography, *The Crack-Up* (1945), from Fitzgerald's unpublished work.

HAWTHORNE, NATHANIEL (1804–1864), together with Edgar Allen Poe, helped to distinguish the short story as a typically American genre, yet Hawthorne was also capable of writing splendid longer works, as he demonstrated in such novels as *The Scarlet Letter* (1850) and *The Marble Faun* (1860). Hawthorne was deeply involved in the critical issues of his day and even served for a time as a government consul in Europe. His novels, however, deal primarily with the isolation of New England souls and are permeated with the Puritan gloom of his New England forebears. Hawthorne's intense introspection allowed him to understand his own and others' motives; his characterizations objectify his discoveries.

HEMINGWAY, ERNEST MILLER (1898–1963) first attracted attention when, as one of the American expatriate writers of the Lost Generation (the Paris group dominated by Gertrude Stein), he depicted the desperate lives of the post–World War I generation. He filled his writing with situations from his own life—his youth, his interest in sports, particularly big-game hunting and bull-fighting, and his experiences in World War I and the Spanish Civil War. Pursuits demanding dedication and discipline commanded his admiration. His prose style, which approaches the rhythm of free verse, has won the admiration of critics and a vast public audience. *A Farewell to Arms* (1929) and *For Whom the Bell Tolls* (1940) remain his most remarkable novels, while *The Fifth Column* (1938) contains his best short stories. Hemingway won the Nobel Prize in 1954 for *The Old Man and the Sea*. His Paris memoirs, *A Moveable Feast* (1964), were published posthumously.

JOYCE, JAMES (1882–1941), literary colossus of the twentieth century, passed the greater part of his life in poverty, his writings misunderstood and rejected. In 1904, Joyce fled Ireland for the Continent, an attempt to dispel the influences of family, church, and homeland. Flight simply proved their powers inescapable. Joyce was entranced by art as pure technique—language, structure, narrative development, and the use of traditional genres—yet his works teem with life, for Joyce, like his fictional counterpart Stephen Dedalus, went "to encounter for the millionth time the reality of experience and to forge in the smithy of my soul the uncreated conscience of my race." His short stories, *Dubliners* (1914), and his novels, *A Portrait of the Artist as a Young Man* (1916), *Ulysses* (1922), and *Finnegan's Wake* (1939), have had a profound effect on modern literature.

LAWRENCE, DAVID HERBERT (1885–1930), the son of a Nottingham coalminer and a former schoolteacher, reveals his early life in what has been called the most celebrated treatment of the Oedipus theme in modern fiction, *Sons and Lovers* (1913). This novel established Lawrence's reputation. The charges of German sympathies (shortly before World War I, he married a divorcée, Frieda von

Richthofen, sister of Baron Manfred von Richthofen, the German military aviator), together with the repudiation of one of his novels, *The Rainbow* (1915), as "filth," drove him out of the country on a search for the ideal society. His frank treatment of sex in *Lady Chatterly's Lover* (1920) forced its private printing and ban from the United States as obscene. Primarily a novelist, Lawrence also wrote significant poetry, short stories, and literary criticism. His *Psychoanalysis and the Unconscious* (1921) and *Fantasia of the Unconscious* (1922) prove him a serious student of psychology.

MANSFIELD, KATHERINE (Kathleen Beauchamp Murray [1888–1923]) could not be contained by her native New Zealand after being exposed to bohemian life in London. On her return to London, she developed stormy but artistically enriching friendships with D. H. Lawrence, Aldous Huxley, Virginia Woolf, and critic John Middleton Murray, whom she later married. With Murray she worked on the publication of various "little magazines," but her most significant work was in the short story, which she endeavored to model along the lines set out by Chekhov, but to which she contributed much that was uniquely her own. Her *Journal* (1927) was published posthumously, as were her collected stories.

MAUPASSANT, HENRI RENÉ ALBERT GUY DE (1850–1893) served a rigid literary apprenticeship under Gustave Flaubert, who taught him and criticized his work for seven years. When at last he published his first story, *Boule de Suif* (1880), the value of such discipline was underscored by general acclaim. During the ten years that followed—until insanity prevented further writing—Maupassant published six novels, numerous travel books, a volume of poetry, and over three hundred short stories. He insisted on *le mot juste*: "whatever . . . we wish to say, there is but one word to express it." For him, a story came only after acute observation: "there is an unexplored side to everything, because we are wont never to use our eyes [except] with the memory of what others before us have thought of the things we see."

MELVILLE, HERMAN (1819–1891) achieved measurable success with his largely autobiographical sea stories *Typee* (1846) and *Omoo* (1847). With the publication of his greatest novels, *Moby Dick* (1851), *Pierre* (1852), and *The Confidence Man* (1857), however, Melville lost his nineteenth-century audience. Friendship with Hawthorne had crystallized Melville's tragic sense of life. He no longer strove simply to entertain, but to convey "visible truth," "the apprehension of the absolute condition of present things as they strike the eye of the man who fears them not, though they do their worst to him." Melville died in obscurity; not until the present century was *Moby Dick* recognized as one of the great novels of the world.

O'Connor, Flannery (1925–1965), after graduating from Women's College of Georgia, worked in the writing program at the State University of Iowa. Her short stories and novels expose the Georgia backwoods society. Her preoccupation with traditional Southern themes and her strong theological bias have come under critical fire as "fashionable" and imitative; defenders find her work stylistically original and indicative of an uncommonly comprehensive theological perspective. Her significant writing includes a novel, *Wise Blood* (1952), and collections of stories, *A Good Man Is Hard to Find* (1955) and *Everything That Rises Must Converge* (1965).

Poe, Edgar Allan (1809–1849) is a name shrouded with a bizarre legend that has confused critical appraisal. The child of itinerant actors, he was raised by foster parents. He was rejected by his foster father and appears to have spent his youth attempting at once to gain approval and to assert his independence. In any case, his defiance and his excesses cost him numerous jobs, his health, and his self-esteem. His attempts to survive on a writer's income resulted in near starvation for him and for his child bride. Whatever he may have been as a man, as a writer he was a giant: a master in creating moods, he wrote notable poetry and criticism and helped to shape the short story into a distinctly American form.

Porter, Katherine Anne (1894–    ), the great-great-great granddaughter of Daniel Boone, spent a precocious childhood in Texas where, she claims, she made life uncomfortable for herself and for those around her. When she chose literature as a profession, she was under no illusion that she could support herself by it, but *Flowering Judas* (1930), her first collection of stories, established her reputation as a finished artist in prose fiction. She has remained a fastidious craftsman, writing few stories, but all of high distinction. Her long expected novel, *Ship of Fools*, appeared in 1962.

Powers, James Earl (1917–    ), an American short-story writer whose works have appeared in *Accent* and *The New Yorker* and several other magazines, has taught at Marquette University and studied in Ireland. He draws heavily on his knowledge of the Roman Catholic Church; his stories generally include church figures and religious questions. Powers is one of the minority of contemporary writers who write with optimism, embracing a movement away from violence and the idea of a menacing society. A writer of considerable talent, his stories have appeared in both the *O. Henry Memorial Award Prize Stories* and *Best American Short Stories*. *Prince of Darkness and Other Stories* (1947) and *The Presence of Grace* (1956) are his first two story collections.

STEELE, WILBUR DANIEL (1886–    ) trained himself in painting at Denver University, the Boston Museum of Fine Arts, and the Académie Julian in Paris. He did not even attempt writing until his year in Paris, and only the successful appearance of "White Horse Winter" in *The Atlantic* (1912) convinced him to devote his talents to prose fiction rather than the graphic arts. His choice proved a happy one; his stories and novels have been widely read. In 1921 he was honored by an unprecedented special prize from the O. Henry Memorial Award Committee for the high quality of his fiction. His ventures in drama— including the dramatization of "How Beautiful with Shoes"—have also been successful.

STEINBECK, JOHN (1902–    ) came into contact with the social problems about which he would later write in his native area, the Salinas Valley in California. He witnessed social upheavals that destroyed the relationship between rural people and the land and saw the painful life of the economically depressed classes. These sights fill his best works. *Tortilla Flat* (1935), his first success, describes down-and-out life in Monterey; *The Grapes of Wrath* (1939), for which he won the Pulitzer Prize in 1940, exposes the plight of the migrant worker. His short stories were collected in an edition titled *The Long Valley* (1938). He won the Nobel Prize for Literature in 1962, primarily for the novel *The Winter of Our Discontent*.

UPDIKE, JOHN (1932–    ), upon graduation from Harvard, began publishing poems and short stories in *The New Yorker*. The poems appearing in his first collection, *The Carpentered Hen* (1958), continued in this early glib style. His prose, especially his novel, *Rabbit Run* (1960), has achieved popular success. Technical adroitness has won him critical acclaim. He is regarded by many as one of the most promising young writers of our time.

# Glossary of Literary Terms

(Cross references are indicated
by SMALL CAPITALS.)

ABSTRACT: Dealing with generalities and ideas, rather than specific, particular objects that evoke vivid mental images. "Honor," "truth," "love" are abstractions. Abstract and general terms are the reverse of CONCRETE and specific terms.

ACT: A major division of a play. Shakespearean DRAMA is normally divided into five acts; modern drama into three. An act, in turn, is usually divided into scenes, in which there is no shift in place and in which the action is continuous in time. On the modern stage, the end of a scene is signalized by the dropping of the curtain or, in the arena theater (theater-in-the-round), by the lowering of the lights.

ALEXANDRINE: A poetic line, usually called a HEXAMETER, that consists of six feet. See METER.

ALLEGORY: Symbolic narration or description in which people, objects, and events directly correspond to other meanings, usually abstract, that they are intended to dramatize.

ALLITERATION: The repetition of initial consonants or consonant sounds in two or more words of a phrase, sentence, or line of poetry. Repetition of initial vowel sounds is occasionally termed alliteration, but is more properly described as ASSONANCE. See CONSONANCE.

ALLUSION: A reference to a historical, literary, or mythical person or event, often used as part of a simile or metaphor.

AMBIGUITY: In the literary sense, the quality of having two or more legitimate meanings that add new dimensions to the word, phrase, or entire work rather than detracting from it.

ANAGNORISIS: See TRAGEDY.

ANAPEST, ANAPESTIC: A poetic foot consisting of two unaccented syllables followed by an accented syllable. See METER.

ANTAGONIST: The character in a work of fiction opposed to the PROTAGONIST. The conflict between them is the occasion of the plot, gives rise to the action.

ANTISTROPHE: One of the stanzas of a triad in a Pindaric ODE or choric song.

ANTITHESIS: A marked contrast of ideas or grammatical elements emphasized by careful balancing of grammatical structure, as in Pope's "Rape of the Lock": "There hero's wits are kept in ponderous vases,/And beau's in snuff-boxes and tweezer cases./There broken vows and death-bed alms are found,/And lovers' hearts with ends of riband bound."

APOSTROPHE: Direct address to a person or object, whether absent or present.

ASIDE: See SOLILOQUY.

ASSONANCE: The repetition of vowels or vowel sounds in two or more words of a phrase, sentence, or line of poetry. See ALLITERATION, CONSONANCE.

ATMOSPHERE: The TONE or mood of a literary composition, which indicates the attitude of the author toward his material. See SETTING.

BALLAD: A short, simple, narrative poem that ordinarily employs a stanza of four lines, alternately of three and four stressed syllables, with only the second and fourth lines rhyming. The folk ballad is anonymous, altered through the ages by individual singers, with a colloquial style and a narrative heavily dependent on dialogue and refrain. The literary ballad (Auden's "The Quarry," for example) is a more complex form written by a single author to present a particular effect or theme.

BALLADE: A French verse form (for instance, Henley's "Ballade of Dead Actors") with three stanzas of eight lines and a concluding stanza, or "envoy," of four lines. The last line of each stanza is the same; only three rhymes are permitted, and no rhyme word may be repeated. The rhyme scheme is thus ababbcbc for the stanzas, and bcbc for the envoy.

BLANK VERSE: Unrhymed poetry, ordinarily iambic pentameter, as in Shakespeare's *Othello* and *Measure for Measure*.

CACOPHONY: The use of unpleasant, discordant sounds for particular effects, as in Pope's "Rape of the Lock": "Gums and pomatums shall his flight restrain," "Or alum styptics with contracting power/Shrink his thin essence." See EUPHONY.

CAESURA: A momentary pause within a line of poetry. See RHYTHM.

CATASTROPHE: The DÉNOUEMENT in tragedy, the conclusion of the conflict. See PLOT.

CATHARSIS: Literally, purgation. In Aristotle's *Poetics*, the audience's purging of their emotions (especially pity and fear) by their vicarious participation in the action of tragic drama. In this sense, the members of the audience assuage their own emotional conflicts by psychological projection, loading their emotions on a scapegoat. In another interpretation, however, they are thought to rid themselves of undue emotion by learning, through observation of the protagonist, how to avoid the destruction he brings upon himself.

CHARACTER: An actor in a story or drama. Character is also the term used to designate the personality or moral disposition of the actor. Thus Macbeth is the main character in Shakespeare's tragedy *Macbeth*; the flaw in his *character* is overweening ambition.

CHORUS: A character or group of characters that comment on the action of a play, often by delivering the PROLOGUE and EPILOGUE, or on the action of a short story or novel (Marlow, in Conrad's "The Lagoon," may be considered a chorus character). In Greek drama, the chorus was a group of actors whose songs furnished both summary and comment on the action at regular intervals in the play. The STROPHE of their choric song was uttered as they moved ritualistically in one direction, the ANTISTROPHE, as they moved in the opposite direction, and the EPODE as they stood still.

CLICHÉ: A stereotype; a trite, worn-out phrase or idea to which fresh, active responses are no longer possible.

CLIMAX: The point of maximum emotional intensity or, in PLOT, the TURNING POINT in the fortunes of the hero.

COINCIDENCE: The accidental coming together of two events, persons, etc. Coincidental occurrences lack any discernible causal relationship.

COMEDY: A type of drama that may or may not aim primarily to evoke laughter, but nevertheless deals with incongruities and inconsistencies of character, action, or traits and in which the various conflicts are resolved "happily," usually by bringing the incongruous elements into accord with some accepted norm of conduct or outlook. FARCE is to comedy what MELODRAMA is to TRAGEDY; farce relies on humorous situations rather than on perception of meaning in human action, and its characters are flat, existing only to take part in the situations that evoke laughter. SLAPSTICK is a type of farce that relies for laughter on pratfalls and beatings in the manner of Punch and Judy. Comedy of manners, on the other hand, relies for its amusing effects on verbal brilliance, wit.

COMEDY OF MANNERS: See COMEDY.

COMPLICATION: In PLOT, the incident or, usually, series of incidents, that lead from the point of attack to the climax. See RISING ACTION.

CONCEIT: A type of METAPHOR, either brief or elaborately extended, that achieves its effects by the ingenuity of the author. The Petrarchan conceit is an extended metaphor, typically comparing a loved one to a rose, a garden, a summer's day, etc. The metaphysical conceit may be identified not only by the startling nature of the comparison, but by its highly intellectual quality. See SIMILE, SYMBOL.

CONCRETE: Giving rise to an immediate sense image of sight, sound, smell, taste, touch. "Grass," "bang," "velvety," "peppermint" are concrete terms. See ABSTRACT.

CONFLICT: The struggle between opposing persons or forces in fiction that constitutes the essential element of PLOT. See ANTAGONIST.

CONNOTATION: The full range of suggestions, associations, or overtones—the meaning beyond DENOTATION—that adheres to a word as the result of personal experience or the attitudes of our society.

CONSONANCE: The repetition of consonants or consonant sounds within two or more words in close proximity. Repetition of initial consonant sounds is properly termed ALLITERATION. See ASSONANCE.

COUPLET: Two successive, rhymed, lines of poetry. See HEROIC COUPLET.

COWLEIAN ODE: See ODE.

DACTYL, DACTYLIC: A poetic foot consisting of an accented syllable followed by two unaccented ones. See METER.

DENOTATION: The explicit, literal meaning of a word, the meaning stripped of personal or general emotional overtones. See CONNOTATION.

DÉNOUEMENT: The conclusion of the PLOT, the outcome of the action, along with any explanations necessary to clear up all misunderstandings.

DEUS EX MACHINA: Literally, "god from a machine," referring to the actor brought in by stage machinery to intervene in the action of ancient Greek and Roman plays; from this, any character or event improbably introduced to resolve a situation.

DIALOGUE: The speech between two or more characters in a narrative or drama; written conversation.

DICTION: The choice of words and the manner of their arrangement peculiar to an author.

DIMETER: A poetic line of two feet. See METER.

DRAMATIC IRONY: See IRONY.

DRAMATIC MONOLOGUE: A poem in which a single speaker (who is not the poet) addresses a silent auditor in the hope of achieving a particular purpose and in the process ironically reveals his character and his hidden motives.

ELEGY: A lyric poem of lament and praise for the dead. Since the poet chooses his stanza form as he wishes and since the feeling and style are equally elevated and dignified, only the subject matter differentiates an elegy like Gray's "Elegy: Written in a Country Churchyard" from a homostrophic ODE. The pastoral elegy (Milton's "Lycidas," Arnold's "Thyrsis") involves certain obligatory elements and a traditional organization: the poet and his dead friend are imagined to be shepherds of classical times; and the poet's expression of grief proceeds from a statement of his loss to an invocation to the Muses, the poet-shepherd's memories of his friend, a description of the funeral procession, the strewing of flowers, and a resolution of the grief in the realization that the friend has achieved immortality.

END-STOPPED LINE: A line of poetry in which there is a distinct, punctuated, structural pause or stop at the end of the line. See RHYTHM.

ENJAMBMENT: A RUN-ON LINE of poetry. See RHYTHM.

ENVIRONMENT: In a broad sense, the SETTING in which the action takes place in fiction, including the place and the social and cultural background.

EPIC: A long poetic narrative concerned with the histories of one or more heroic characters engaged in an action of great significance. Certain conventional elements are customarily involved. The epic poem begins at or near the most important action of the narrative (*in medias res*), shifting then to incidents that led up to this climax and to those that follow it; the style is elevated, making use of a formal invocation to the Muses, a specific statement of the theme, long formal similes, genealogies of noble figures, catalogues of ships or troops involved in the action, and numerous references to the gods' participation. The folk epic (*Beowulf, The Odyssey*) is concerned simply with great actions in the heroic age, whereas the literary epic (*The Aeneid, The Argonautica, Paradise Lost*) demonstrates more conscious literary control by a single author rather than growth in an oral tradition. The mock epic ("The Rape of the Lock") is a burlesque form that applies all the traditional epic elements to an action of trivial significance.

EPILOGUE: A concluding statement, added to a play or novel, that gives information or provides comment that properly lies outside the bounds of the work itself. In eighteenth-century plays, it was often written by someone other than the author and delivered after the curtain.

EPISODE: An incident complete in itself, yet part of a larger action. In Greek drama, an episode is the action that takes place between two choruses, roughly comparable to a scene in modern drama.

EPITHET: An adjective used to single out a main characteristic of a person or thing, as in Homer's "ox-eyed Hera" or "cloud-gathering Zeus." A transferred epithet is this kind of modifier applied in an unusual way, as in Milton's "Lycidas" ("blind mouths") or Bridges' "Low Barometer" ("sightless footsteps pad the floor").

EPODE: The third stanza of a triad, different from the other two, in a Pindaric ODE or a choric song.

ESSAY: A relatively brief expository composition dealing with a limited subject.

EUPHONY: Any pattern of agreeable, harmonious sounds. The opposite of CACOPHONY.

EXPOSITION: The portion of the PLOT that introduces the characters, sets the tone, and furnishes whatever information about the situation is necessary to understand the subsequent action.

FALLING ACTION: The portion of the dramatic PLOT that leads from the climax to the dénouement.

FARCE: See COMEDY.

FEMININE ENDING: At the end of a poetic line, a word ending with an unstressed syllable. See RHYME.

FEMININE RHYME: See RHYME.

FIGURATIVE LANGUAGE: Language that conveys meaning by the use of an explicit or implied comparison with something else, as in such figures, or TROPES, as the METAPHOR, SIMILE, or SYMBOL.

FLASHBACK: The insertion of antecedent details after an action has started.

FLAT CHARACTER: A character with one dominant trait that governs his actions and makes those actions consistent. E. M. Forster, who invented the term, divided all characters in fiction into flat and round, identifying flat characters with the "humours" of seventeenth-century drama, with types, or with caricatures. A flat character is simple rather than complex; but simplicity is relative, with caricature at one extreme and an individual with considerably more depth, such as Polonius, in *Hamlet*, at the other. Flat characters far outnumber round in fiction. See ROUND CHARACTERS.

FOLK BALLAD: See BALLAD.

FOLK EPIC: See EPIC.

FOOT: In poetry, the basic metrical unit, a pattern of either two or three stressed and unstressed syllables. See METER.

FORESHADOWING: An intimation of events to come.

FREE VERSE: Poetry that does not use rhyme or regular meter as a means of achieving coherence.

GENERALIZATION: An inclusive statement of an idea in an expository essay that is developed by particulars.

GENRE: A term meaning "kind" or "type," used to label both the broad categories of literature (drama, essay, novel, poetry, short story) and the particular species within each category (dramatic monologue, elegy, ode, sonnet, etc.).

HALF RHYME: See RHYME.

HAMARTIA: See TRAGEDY.

HEPTAMETER: A poetic line of seven feet. See METER.

HERO: The central character in a work of fiction, without regard to his moral traits. See PROTAGONIST.

HEROIC COUPLET: Two successive, rhymed, iambic pentameter poetic lines.

HEXAMETER: A poetic line of six feet, sometimes called an ALEXANDRINE. See METER.

HOMOSTROPHIC ODE: See ODE.

HORATIAN ODE: See ODE.

HUBRIS: See TRAGEDY.

HYPERBOLE: See IRONY.

IAMB, IAMBIC: A poetic foot consisting of an unaccented syllable followed by an accented one. See METER.

IMAGERY: In a general sense, any figure of speech or description that helps the reader imaginatively to see, feel, taste, hear, smell, or to experience the sensation of physical movement; more specifically, FIGURATIVE LANGUAGE.

INCREMENTAL REPETITION: Repetition, with variations that provide new information, of one or more lines of a poem or ballad, as in the first two lines of "Edward, Edward."

INTERNAL RHYME: See RHYME.

INTRIGUE: Plot in the drama, especially a plot that revolves around a situation in which one character is completely unaware of the machinations of another.

INVERSION: An unusual twisting of the normal grammatical order of a sentence so that certain elements may be stressed, as in Shakespeare's Sonnet LXXIII: "That time of year thou mayst in me behold." In the hands of less skillful writers, the device often becomes an awkward affectation, purposeless except as a means of ending with the proper rhyming word.

IRONY: A kind of figurative language involving a relationship between the reality described and the terms used to describe it. At least three main types of irony may be distinguished. Verbal irony is based on an incongruous relationship between the apparent and real meanings of a statement. At one extreme is understatement, in which the speaker means much more than he says; at the other extreme is hyperbole, in which the speaker uses extravagantly exaggerated terms; between these extremes are various degrees of verbal incongruity, often no more than a nuance of tone. Structural irony is a principle of organization rather than a kind of statement. In its simplest form, this type of irony is a sharp contrast of events or situations; more subtly, it may involve only minor shades of difference or the collapse of several scattered events into a single moment, as in Jarrell's "The Death of the Ball Turret Gunner." Dramatic irony refers to a situation in a play or a dramatic monologue in which the audience more fully understands the significance of words or actions than do the characters.

ITALIAN SONNET: See SONNET.

LITERARY BALLAD: See BALLAD.

LITERARY EPIC: See EPIC.

LOCAL COLOR: Setting that depends heavily upon the peculiarities of a particular region for its effect.

LYRIC: Originally "a song" (sung to the accompaniment of a lyre), the term now applies to any expository poem revealing the personal response of the poet. See ELEGY, ODE, SONNET.

MASCULINE ENDING: At the end of a poetic line, a word ending with an accented syllable. See RHYME.

MASCULINE RHYME: See RHYME.

MELODRAMA: See TRAGEDY.

METAPHOR: A figure of speech that conveys meaning by use of an implied comparison, whether in a single word or phrase or in a lengthy parallel (an extended metaphor). See SIMILE, SYMBOL.

METAPHYSICAL CONCEIT: See CONCEIT.

METER: The pattern of stressed and unstressed syllables in poetry, described in terms of the basic unit of the pattern, the FOOT, and the number of units, or feet, in each line. Five major types of poetic foot appear in English poetry: the IAMB, an unaccented syllable followed by an accented one (- '); the TROCHEE, an accented syllable followed by an unaccented one (' -); the DACTYL, an accented syllable followed by two unaccented ones (' - -); the ANAPEST, two unaccented syllables followed by one accented one (- - '); and the SPONDEE, two accented syllables (' '). The number of feet in a line may vary from one to as many as eight. MONOMETER denotes one foot in a line; DIMETER, two; TRIMETER, three; TETRAMETER, four; PENTAMETER, five; HEXAMETER, six; HEPTAMETER, seven, and OCTAMETER, eight. A line of poetry is thus described as iambic pentameter, trochaic hexameter, etc.

METONYMY: A figure of speech that describes one thing by reference to another very closely related to it but not, strictly speaking, part of it. See Robert Bridges' description in "Low Barometer" of a thing "whose sightless footsteps pad the floor,/ Whose fearful trespass mounts the stair." Literally, "footsteps" cannot walk and "trespass" cannot climb, but Bridges has used what we hear in place of the feet that make sounds, and the result of an action (trespass) in place of what performs the action.

METRICAL ROMANCE: Any verse narrative of adventure, on a less elevated plane than the events of an EPIC, that is told for its own intrinsic popular interest rather than for its significance as history or mythical truth. Originally, a French form categorized by subject matter (e.g., The Matter of France, Matter of Rome, Matter of Britain).

MOCK EPIC: See EPIC.

MONOMETER: A poetic line of one foot. See METER.

MOTIVATION: The purpose that dominates a character in fiction and gives rise to his actions.

NOVEL: Prose fiction of considerable length showing characters in action, and capable of greater complexity in both character and plot than the short story.

NOVELETTE: A short novel; its scope lies beyond the unity of effect of the short story.

OBJECTIVE: A literary work is regarded as objective when there is little or no intrusion of the author, either by way of self-revelation or interpretation of events. Thus the drama is largely objective, since the dramatist usually presents his characters entirely by speech and action, without comment, and without identifying himself with any of them. In an objective point of view in narrative, the author relies heavily upon dialogue and sense details without entering the mind of any of the characters. See SUBJECTIVE.

OCTAMETER: A poetic line of eight feet. See METER.

OCTAVE: See SONNET.

ODE: A lyric poem characterized by lofty feeling, dignified style, and organization according to one of three patterns. The Pindaric, or regular, ode consists of a series of three-stanza units known as TRIADS. Two of these, the STROPHE and ANTISTROPHE, are identical in number of lines, number of accented syllables in each line, and in rhyme scheme; the third stanza, the EPODE, markedly contrasts in one or more elements to the other stanzas of the triad. The Horatian, or homostrophic, ode has none of these complex variations. The poet chooses the form for one stanza and repeats it throughout the poem. The Cowleian, or irregular, ode, the least rigid of the three forms, consists of any number of stanzas, each different from the others in number of lines, number of accented syllables in each line, and rhyme scheme, as in Wordsworth's "Ode: Intimations of Immortality."

OFF RHYME: See RHYME.

OMNISCIENT: The POINT OF VIEW in fiction in which the author gets inside the mind of any of his characters at will.

ONOMATOPOEIA, ONOMATOPOETIC: The use of words whose sounds duplicate those of the object or action that is described, as when Keats writes that the ocean "*Gluts* twice ten thousand caverns."

OTTAVA RIMA: A stanza of eight iambic pentameter lines rhyming *abababcc*, as in Byron's "Don Juan."

OXYMORON: A type of ANTITHESIS that brings together two sharply contrasting terms in a single phrase, as in Milton's "darkness visible" or "bad eminence." See PARADOX.

PARADOX: A figure of speech that links apparently contradictory terms in a single statement that is, in fact, true. OXYMORON resembles paradox, but whereas the first is a phrase, the second is a predication.

PASTORAL ELEGY: See ELEGY.

PATHETIC FALLACY: John Ruskin's term for the practice of endowing nature with human characteristics, particularly emotions. See CONCEIT, PERSONIFICATION.

PENTAMETER: A poetic line of five feet. See METER.

PERIPETEIA: See TRAGEDY.

PERSONIFICATION: A figure of speech based on the assumption that animals, abstract ideas, or things have human characteristics. In a sense, personification is a kind of metaphor equating an object or an abstraction with a human being.

PETRARCHAN CONCEIT: See CONCEIT.

PETRARCHAN, or ITALIAN, SONNET: See SONNET.

PICARESQUE: A form of fiction that takes its name from the Spanish "*picaro*," or "rogue." The action is linear, episodic, and the protagonist, who lives largely by his wits, is engaged in a series of adventures that are often amusing and always related with realistic detail.

PINDARIC ODE: See ODE.

PLOT: A plan of action in narrative and drama containing a conflict and its resolution. The conflict arises out of circumstances that create an unstable situation for the protagonist and proceeds through a series of related actions until some conclusion has been reached. The divisions of the plot, particularly as they apply to the drama, have been called EXPOSITION, POINT OF ATTACK, RISING ACTION (COMPLICATION), CLIMAX (TURNING POINT), FALLING ACTION, and DÉNOUEMENT (or, especially in tragedy, CATASTROPHE). Plot requires a causal relation between events; when this is lacking, the action is called episodic. For plausibility plot requires MOTIVATION, purpose behind the action of the characters. Plot creates SUSPENSE, the desire to discover how the action will turn out.

PLOT-RIDDEN CHARACTER: A character in fiction who acts in a way that is inconsistent with his capabilities or personality because of the demands of the plot.

POETIC DICTION: The particular choice of words and manner of their arrangement regarded by certain authors as the only language refined enough to be used in poetry.

POINT OF ATTACK: That point in the plot at which the complication begins, the event that disturbs the *status quo*.

POINT OF VIEW: The angle from which a story is told, which may be personal or impersonal. In a narrative the author may choose to relate events as they are seen and experienced by one of the characters, by viewing the action completely from the outside, or by injecting himself into the narrative as the one who sees all, knows all, and tells all.

PROBLEM PLAY: A drama that directs attention to a particular sociological problem, as *Hedda Gabler* does to the problem of woman's proper place in late nineteenth-century society.

PROLOGUE: An introduction to a play, novel, or other literary work.

PROSODY: The study of versification. See METER, RHYME, RHYTHM.

PROTAGONIST: The central character in a work of fiction, the hero. In the ensuing conflict his opponent is called the ANTAGONIST.

PURPLE PASSAGE: A passage of verse or prose that is highly emotional, and so constructed by various stylistic devices that it calls attention to itself out of context.

PYRRHIC: A poetic foot consisting of two unaccented syllables.

QUATRAIN: Four lines of poetry linked as a unit by rhyme, usually in the pattern *abab* or *abba*.

REFRAIN: A phrase or verse regularly repeated in a song or poem.

RHYME: Similarity or identity of sound in two or more words, usually the last words of poetic lines. Masculine rhyme is identity of final, accented syllables of rhyming words, as in "heard," "bird," or "seas," "Hebrides"; feminine rhyme is identity of the last two syllables, the first accented, the second unaccented, as in "replying," "dying," or "hopping," "stopping";

triple rhyme is identity of the last three syllables of rhyming words, as in "intellectual," "hen-pecked you all"; slant rhyme, off rhyme or half rhyme, is an approximation rather than an identity of sounds; internal rhyme is identity of sounds in two words within a single line of poetry.

RHYME ROYAL: A stanza of seven iambic pentameter lines rhyming *ababbcc*.

RHYME SCHEME: The order or pattern of rhymes in a poem, described by designating the first rhyming word and all others that rhyme with it *a*; the first new rhyming word and all others that rhyme with it *b*; the next different rhyming word *c*; and so on. Words that do not rhyme with any others are usually marked *x*. A four-line poem in which the first and third lines and the second and fourth lines rhyme would be described as *abab*.

RHYTHM: In poetry, the pattern of phrasing in a line, stanza, or an entire poem. The term should be clearly distinguished from METER, which describes only the pattern of stressed and unstressed syllables in a line. Rhythm is established by the CAESURA, a momentary pause within a line that may or may not be indicated by punctuation; by the presence or absence of END-STOPPED LINES, in which there is a distinct, punctuated, structural pause or stop at the end of the line; and by RUN-ON LINES (also known as ENJAMBMENT), in which there is no structural division or pause between the end of one line and the beginning of the next.

RISING ACTION: The COMPLICATION of action between the point of attack and the climax. See PLOT.

ROMANTIC: In literature, a term often used as the opposite of realistic. Romantic literature is, in general, literature somewhat at a remove from ordinary life, with both setting and action tending toward the ideal rather than the real.

RONDEAU: A French verse form (see Dobson's rondeau, "You Bid Me Try") consisting of thirteen lines with only two rhymes. The first phrase of line 1 reappears as a refrain in lines 9 and 13. The rondel, a variant form, consists of fourteen lines, two rhymes, and uses lines 1 and 2 as a refrain repeated twice in the poem, as lines 7 and 8, and 13 and 14.

ROUND CHARACTER: A character of some complexity, whose actions are not as predictable as those of a FLAT CHARACTER. A round character is shown to have varying, and often contradictory, traits, which are subject to change by circumstances, so that he is capable of growth and development. Since all of this demands time, round characters almost never appear in the shorter forms of fiction.

RUN-ON LINE: A line of poetry that has no structural division or pause at the end of it, but leads directly into the following line. See RHYTHM.

SCENE: In drama, a division of an act, marked usually by the dropping of the curtain on the modern stage. Action in a scene is continuous, with no shift in place. In narrative a scene is an incident in which the action is presented in detail and that, like a scene in drama, is continuous in time and action.

SENTIMENTALITY: Any attempt on the part of an author to make his reader react more emotionally than the content of the work warrants.

SESTET: See SONNET.

SESTINA: A French verse form so incredibly complicated that to follow its requirements and yet write something intelligible is a major *tour de force*. See Kipling's "Sestina of the Tramp Royal." The sestina consists of six six-line stanzas and one final three-line stanza. The stanzas do not rhyme; instead, each ends with the same six words used in an entirely different order in each of the first five stanzas according to a regular progression. The last, three-line, stanza must use as end-words the fifth, third, and first end-words of the first stanza (in that order) and must include in the middle of each of the three lines the other three end-words of stanza one.

SETTING: The specific place, time—all that makes up the physical background in which the action of a narrative or drama takes place. It is the total environment that surrounds the characters in fiction.

SHAKESPEAREAN SONNET: See SONNET.

SIMILE: A figure of speech in which one thing is explicitly compared to another by the use of "like," "as," "so," etc. See METAPHOR, SYMBOL.

SLANT RHYME: See RHYME.

SLAPSTICK: See COMEDY.

SOLILOQUY: A speech delivered by a character in a play when he is alone on stage. It is not an aside delivered to the audience, but it has the effect of permitting the audience to know the character's thoughts. Proper justification or plausibility ordinarily requires that the soliloquy be spoken as a result of great stress, and this in turn would seem to imply conflict within the character.

SONNET: A poem of fourteen lines (usually iambic pentameter), rhyming according to one of two main patterns. The Italian sonnet consists of two four-line units—the octave—followed by a six-line unit—the sestet. The rhyme scheme of the octave is always *abba abba*; the scheme of the sestet may be *cdcdcd, cdecde,* or a similar variation. The organization of the poem usually corresponds to the divisions of octave and sestet, often with the octave posing a question that is answered in the sestet. The Shakespearean sonnet consists of three four-line units, or quatrains, followed by a couplet, the entire poem rhyming *abab cdcd efef gg*. The organization of material in the poem may or may not correspond to these divisions. Among other variations, the poet may choose to combine the first two quatrains into a kind of octave, and the last quatrain and couplet into a sestet, or he may treat each quatrain as a separate unit of meaning and use the couplet as summary and brief comment.

SPENSERIAN STANZA: A stanza of nine lines, the first eight iambic pentameter, the last an ALEXANDRINE (see METER), rhyming *ababbcbcc*.

SPONDEE: A poetic foot consisting of two accented syllables. See METER.

STANZA: Two or more lines of poetry (a single line is properly called a VERSE) unified by meter, rhyme, thought, or all of these. See COUPLET, OTTAVA RIMA, QUATRAIN, RHYME ROYAL, SPENSERIAN STANZA, TERCET, TERZA RIMA.

STOCK CHARACTER: A type character found repeatedly in literature, such as the faithful servant or the overpossessive mother. Stock characters, although exhibiting the conventional traits that make them readily identifiable as characters belonging in the tradition of the genre, are often drawn with highly individual traits as well, so that they become memorable in themselves. Thus Partridge, the servant of Tom Jones, in Fielding's novel *Tom Jones*, belongs to a clearly recognizable type in the picaresque story but is, at the same time, a unique individual.

STREAM OF CONSCIOUSNESS: A literary technique that became popular with James Joyce, in which the author of a narrative portrays the thoughts of a character in an almost objective fashion as they presumably run through his mind, following no order but the pattern of association and recollection and usually without recognizable syntax. Another name for stream of consciousness is "interior monologue."

STREAM OF EXPERIENCE: The POINT OF VIEW in fiction that looks out at the action through the eyes and mind of one of the characters, so that all events are filtered through this one consciousness.

STROPHE: One of the stanzas of a triad in a Pindaric ODE or choric song.

SUBJECTIVE: Literature is normally regarded as subjective when it reflects the attitude and personality of the author. Thus lyrical poetry is subjective in comparison with epic poetry, for it is often highly personal, whereas in the epic the author merely presents characters in action without entering the picture himself. See OBJECTIVE.

SUSPENSE: The uncertainty that comes about because of conflict, the desire to know the outcome of the actions of characters who have aroused our interest.

SYMBOL: In literature, a symbol is a word or phrase, an object or action, that has significance over and beyond what it is itself; this significance suggested by the context. Whether briefly described or developed in great detail, the symbol is a figure of speech making use of an implicit comparison in which the second term is more carefully developed than in METAPHOR. Literary symbols are seldom to be equated exactly with what they suggest; they carry layers of suggestion. See SIMILE.

SYNECDOCHE: A form of metaphor that describes something by reference to one small but important part of it, as in Wordsworth's "London, 1802": "altar, sword, and pen,/ Fireside, the heroic wealth of hall and bower."

TERCET: Three successive, rhymed lines of poetry.

TERZA RIMA: A pattern of three-line stanzas successively linked by rhyme in the pattern of Shelley's "Ode to the West Wind": *aba bcb cdc,* etc. See RHYME SCHEME.

TETRAMETER: A poetic line of four feet. See METER.

THEME: The unifying idea underlying a literary work, the thesis.

TONE: The attitude of the author toward his subject, indicated by the diction, rhythm, and other matters of style and structure. The tone of a short story, for instance, might be serious or playful or foreboding. See ATMOSPHERE.

TRAGEDY: A type of drama in which the protagonist engages in conflict with overwhelming forces within or outside himself, suffers in the conflict, learns about himself and the forces arrayed against him, and often dies. In Aristotle's commentary on Greek tragedy, *hamartia* is the tragic flaw, weakness, or mistake; *hubris,* or arrogance and pride, is one common type of tragic flaw, though not the only one; *peripeteia* is a reversal in which an action produces a result opposite to that intended; and *anagnorisis* is the recognition both of who a character really is (Oedipus' revelation concerning his birth) and of the general truths to be learned from his conflict and suffering. Melodrama, one might add, bears the same relationship to tragedy as farce or slapstick bear to COMEDY. Melodrama involves the superficial characteristics of tragedy, the noble versus the villainous characters, the horror and suffering, the conflicts of tremendous proportions, but it presents these as ends in themselves, not as means of presenting the insights about man that are integral to tragedy.

TRIAD: A unit, consisting of three stanzas, in a Pindaric ODE or choric song.

TRIMETER: A poetic line of three feet. See METER.

TRIOLET: A French verse form (see Bridges' triolet, "When First We Met") consisting of eight lines and only two rhymes. Line 1 reappears as line 4 and line 7; line 2 reappears as line 8.

TRIPLE RHYME: See RHYME.

TROCHEE, TROCHAIC: A poetic foot consisting of an accented syllable followed by an unaccented one. See METER.

TROPE: See FIGURATIVE LANGUAGE.

TURNING POINT: The point in the PLOT that marks a change in the fortunes of the protagonist and from which, at least in retrospect, the outcome of the conflict is discernible. In tragedy, it marks the high point in the fortunes of the hero. See CLIMAX.

UNDERSTATEMENT: See IRONY.

UNITIES: The dramatic unities traditionally involve action, time, and place: coherent action, with a clear beginning, middle, and end (some have therefore suggested that a subplot violates this coherence); a single day; and one place. Shakespeare, of course, brilliantly violates all of these except the first.

VERSE: A single line of poetry, distinguished from the STANZA.

VILLANELLE: A complex French verse form (see Dowson, "Villanelle of the Poet's Road"), consisting of six stanzas totaling nineteen lines—the first five stanzas being each three lines long and the last, four. Line 1 of the poem must reappear as a refrain in lines 6, 12, and 18; line 2 must reappear as lines 9, 15, and 19. Only two rhymes are permitted.